THE CURIOUS WORLD OF TWINS

Other Books by Vincent and Margaret Gaddis

The Strange World of Animals and Pets

Books by Vincent Gaddis

Mysterious Fires and Lights
Invisible Horizons
The Wide World of Magic

Books by Margaret Gaddis

No Fire Can Warm Me
As M. P. Rea:
A Curtain for Crime
Compare These Dead
Death of an Angel
Blackout at Rehearsal
Death Walks the Dry Tortugas

THE CURIOUS WORLD OF TWINS

Vincent and Margaret Gaddis

HAWTHORN BOOKS, INC.

PUBLISHERS

NEW YORK

To all twins—Ruby
and Ruth, Laura and Elizabeth,
Jack and Henry, and all others—
who led us into their wonderful
world of mystery and marvel:
"twindom"

THE CURIOUS WORLD OF TWINS

Copyright © 1972 by Vincent and Margaret Gaddis. Copyright under International and Pan-American Copyright Conventions. All rights reserved, including the right to reproduce this book, or portions thereof, in any form, except for the inclusion of brief quotations in a review. All inquiries should be addressed to Hawthorn Books, Inc., 70 Fifth Avenue, New York, New York 10011. This book was manufactured in the United States of America and published simultaneously in Canada by Prentice-Hall of Canada, Limited, 1870 Birchmount Road, Scarborough, Ontario. Library of Congress Catalog Card Number: 71-179116.

1 2 3 4 5 6 7 8 9 10

PREFACE AND
ACKNOWLEDGMENTS

This book began with a magazine article on extrasensory perception in twins and the correspondence resulting from it. Soon our files were bulging with data and stories of multiple births. Later when we were in Rome in September, 1965, we were granted the privilege of an interview with Professor Luigi Gedda and his associate, Professor Marco Milani-Comparetti.

They graciously showed us throughout the Istituto di Genetica Medica (The Twin Institute) of the University of Rome, renowned for its unique beauty as well as its scientific prestige. We saw the library with its gleaming brass spiral stair, the museum, the testing devices such as the "stinkometer" they designed, and the five lovely bedrooms where the little twins who come in from the countryside are cared for by the white-robed nuns. All this jewel-like elegance is in sharp contrast to austere American counterparts, which have no murals in lecture halls and certainly no brass door handles symbolizing twin embryos.

It left an unforgettable impression, which intrigued us still more with the importance of twin phenomena and led us to begin our book in earnest.

We are indebted to several scientists, doctors, and medical personnel for answering questions, for reading and checking certain chapters in the manuscript, and for lending us the latest material clarifying recent discoveries in blood typing, chromosomal abnormalities, and those newly found "mosaic" individuals who are not quite twins.

The only reason we do not mention these friendly experts by name is because they might be embarrassed by other parts of the manuscript which they have not read—and which contain material that their own disciplines consider far-out or speculative.

We are also indebted to many researchers in the psychic and related fields who have sent us cases and references involving twins—and particularly to Dr. J. B. Rhine, of the Institute for Parapsychology, Foundation for Research on the Nature of Man, at the University of North Carolina, for his kindness in agreeing to review Chapters 6 and 8 of this book. In fact, we quote, with permission, from a letter we received from him:

> It is an important service to science to assemble these amazing cases of twin coincidences. The publication of them also helps to awaken wider interest in the reporting of similar cases to those who are interested, as many of us are, in studying them for the indications they may give of the many things we do not yet understand about man's nature.
>
> Of course, the same service could be rendered with many other close interpersonal relations among people, but nothing is so interesting, perhaps, as the context of twinship. When something happens to twins, it is dramatized in our interest to a remarkable degree, and in making more of it we are likely to help along the discovery of what really goes on there.
>
> I cannot and I need not presume to have in mind all the many challenging questions that arise from these exceptional coincidences. They cover many fields of scientific and social interests, but for my own field of parapsychology [the study of the extrasensory and extramotor exchange a person has with his surroundings] these more exceptional twin reports are rich and challenging material, indeed. Naturally, they vary widely in almost every respect. Some of the more unusual ones have to be found in many recurrences and under the kind of responsible record-keeping such as a good hospital maintains before they will be taken seriously by the scientists on an evidential basis. But cases like the Eller twins seem to qualify on that score.
>
> But there is another value for science that must not be overlooked: The first stimulus that initiates a line of inquiry can be given by a case that could not stand alone at all, but it may open the eyes of an interested scholar who will look for similar cases, and with numbers he will

look for an hypothesis, and then for an experiment. And so the trail of science is followed from a starting point of only transient importance.

That I think is the way to look at this collection. Here are many good tips for the exploring scientist, tips that could lead to research of great importance if carefully checked and verified.

Sincerely,
J. B. Rhine

Beyond the individuals and groups already mentioned, we must express our gratitude to astrologers and graphologists and their societies, in the United States and abroad, whose case histories and opinions have been of the greatest interest. Nor can we forget individual twins and twin societies—the National Organization of Mothers of Twins Clubs, Inc., and the International Twins Associations, Inc., who have patiently answered questions and contributed intriguing life stories.

In fact, without the cooperation of hundreds of correspondents and advisers, our book could never have reached print. We thank them gratefully. A very special tribute must go to our editor, Charles N. Heckelmann, for his patience and skill throughout the unusual complexities we encountered.

Vincent and Margaret Gaddis
Escondido, California

CONTENTS

Illustrations appear after page 114.

THE CURIOUS WORLD OF TWINS

1   TWINS FANTASTIC

It was a day for boys—a day for boyish ecstasies. For twelve-year-old Jud, the Nebraska county fair was "really somethin'." He was jubilant as a jaybird, his pa would have said, and Jud's delight was in his eyes. It was the first time Pa had turned him loose at the fair on his own. He had fifty cents to spend as he pleased, and that was a lot of money to a farm boy in that Depression summer in the early 1930's. And though his jeans were worn and his shabby shoes already gray with dust, Jud's elation shone through his scrubbed face.

The odor of sizzling hot dogs, fresh popcorn, and roasting peanuts tantalized him, but there was a good lunch waiting for him in Mom's basket in the Women's Building, and a fellow could always eat. Here were more tempting marvels—like the Ferris wheel and the sword-swallower. He thrust his hand into his pocket and fingered the precious fifty-cent piece, then turned and ran toward the bandstand. That was free! And while he listened he could choose which of the dazzling prospects he would enjoy first.

Dodging right and left through the crowd, he suddenly collided with another boy, then jerked to a bewildered halt. Golly!! Was he looking at his own self? No, it couldn't be. Though their faces were as alike as two buffalo nickels, the other Jud was wearing city clothes.

"Jeepers!" gasped the city boy. "We must be twins!"

To Jud the voice even sounded like his. They stared at each other for a moment, and wide grins spread over their faces. Then above the music and the noise, the grins exploded into laughter.

"I'm Harry!" said the city boy. "What's your name?"

"I'm Jud!" Then, after a puzzled look: "Gee, Harry, *you* didn't come from an orphanage, *too,* did you?"

The second of silence between them blocked out the blare of the band. Jud felt the suspense within him like a balloon about to burst, and when he saw Harry nod, he knew that speech was momentarily impossible for Harry, too.

"Jeepers!" Harry exclaimed finally. "Then we gotta be twins, Jud! Let's find our folks and make them tell!"

Jud pulled back, his face suddenly sober. "Sure, Harry. We will. But there's plenty of time. I don't know where my folks'll be. I'm supposed to meet them at five o'clock. Let's just have fun together first!" And he put out the hand that didn't have the wart to grab Harry's fingers in his as they bounded off.

What a day it was! Now it was really filled with boyish ecstasies. Jud showed his sweaty half-dollar, and Harry pulled a five-dollar bill from his pocket. When Jud gasped at the sight of so much money and seemed reluctant to share it, Harry swore he would tear it up if they didn't go "even stephen."

They rode the Dodge-em, the Ferris wheel, and the caterpillar. They saw the Alligator Girl and the Armless-Legless Wonder. But the greatest wonder of all was the discovery every few moments that they were think-alikes as well as look-alikes. In those moments their grins would explode in laughter and the joy of the discovery.

"Gosh!" they would exclaim in unison, "we *must* be twins! From now on, wherever we are, we'll be together, won't we?"

And that was the best part of all. In his whole life Jud had never been so happy. His folks were good to him, and he loved them, but this warm feeling of oneness, of another self who shared all his feelings, his thoughts—this was something he'd never known could happen. And it lasted all day.

Later in the afternoon, when nearly all their money was spent, they were throwing baseballs at a clown's head when a woman's voice nearby shrieked, *"Hair-ee-ee!"*

There was anger in the voice and something like fear. Jud's heart dropped to his shoes. He saw a couple whose fine clothes and outraged faces made him feel lower than a worm in his Pa's cornfield. They stared at him, their faces white. Quickly, then, they grabbed Harry, one on each side of him, and marched off. Harry turned once before they disappeared in the crowd and called over his shoulder, "So long, Jud! I'll be seeing you!"

The lump in Jud's throat was still there when he met his folks, and it kept him from eating the fried chicken and deviled eggs Mom had fixed.

"You ain't sick, are you, Jud?" she asked anxiously.

Jud kept his eyes down, but finally it had to come out. "Mom, Pa, did I have a twin brother?"

He saw the answer in their eyes. Yes, Pa said, he'd had a twin brother at the orphanage. But things were tough on the farm then, and some city folks wanted the other boy.

Jud told them then about his day and the wonderful discovery he had made. "Can I go see him?"

"They're rich city folks, Jud. You wouldn't be welcome."

Pa's tone was final, and it marked the end of all hope.

A Strange Reunion

What is the opposite of ecstasy? Bitterness? Heartache? In the ten years that followed, Jud never again knew a single day that could match it. He buried the hurt deep, and there it remained until the night he took refuge in a foxhole on Guadalcanal. Jud was a marine then, and the army had come ashore that day. By night the machine guns, rifles, and mortars were creating a deafening roar. Suddenly there was a flare that lit up the whole scene just as Harry, his twin, dived into the hole beside him.

"Well, what do you know?" he said with a grin. "How're you doing, fellow? My double, Jud!"

Double, he said. That told Jud that Harry's folks hadn't leveled with him.

Ducking cautiously under their ponchos, they stared at each other's features in the flare of a match. Then in the darkness they tried to bridge the years. Harry was married, he said. He had gone to the university and had been made a captain in the army.

Jud felt the vast gulf between them. Harry was a long way from being a plain marine, and a farm boy at that. Jud couldn't tell him now that they were really brothers. There was no reason for Harry to be proud of *him!* But Harry insisted on exchanging addresses and promised to get in touch again "when this damn war is over."

Later that night, when the Japanese barrage had quieted down, Harry slid out of the foxhole and joined his men. And the next morning Jud's outfit was transferred to another sector. That was in August, 1942.

To Jud, the meeting and the entire strange night seemed like a dream in the days that followed. Nearly three years passed.

It was April, 1945, on Okinawa. The war had gone on a long, long time. Once again it was dark and in the midst of battle. He was lying prone behind a big rock, watching for any movement on the open ground before him.

Presently he could hear someone breathing in grunts like a man close to death. Was it an enemy soldier trying to outfox him? Knife at the ready, he crawled forward cautiously, waiting for a flare. Then in a flash of light he saw a man in army uniform, huddled in a heap.

"Wait, man," said Jud. "I'm going back for help. I'll get the medic."

"Jud?" the man groaned. "It's you, Jud, isn't it?"

In the light of the next flare Jud saw it was Harry. Blood came from his mouth when he spoke, and Jud couldn't hide from him the knowledge that it was too late to seek aid. Jud held his brother in his arms while he gasped something about his wife, then, "Gosh, Jud! I wish we really were brothers—twins!" His head dropped, and his eyes closed.

"We are, Harry, we are!" Jud cried as he held his brother close. Over and over he repeated it. "We are, Harry! We're brothers! We're twins!" He told him he'd known it from the first day, but hadn't dared admit it on Guadalcanal, with Harry so far above him in rank and education. He talked fast now, but Harry's eyes were glazed slits, and he'd stopped breathing. Jud knew Harry was gone, and his words faded into the black battle-loud night.

A Message Received

Months later Jud was shipped home to a separation center near Laguna Beach, California. Every night the U.S.O. Club was jammed with returning veterans. Among the local citizens who gave freely of their time and talents was a doctor, Arthur Trevenning Harris, and Kathryn Olsen, an artist. Miss Olsen sketched portraits in charcoal, then at her own expense mailed the sketches to the GIs' homes. Dr. Harris served with other Rotary Club members as a waiter or dish-washer or at other odd jobs.

One evening at the club Dr. Harris noticed a sad-faced young marine talking to Miss Olsen. She nodded encouragingly, like the mother-confessor she was, but as she sketched, the boy could not seem to smile back. Low in his mind and forlorn, the doctor rea-soned. But things were rushed at the U.S.O., and he had forgotten the marine when Kay Olsen tugged at his arm.

"Dr. Harris, please come and listen!" She nodded toward the marine still beside her easel, his head buried in his hands. "I don't know what to make of it, Doctor. I—I'm scared!"

She led the doctor over and introduced them. The boy was shaking his head, his eyes dazed.

"He—he's so upset!" Kay's voice trembled. "But I just sketched what I *saw!* Only—how could I have seen that, when *he's* a marine?" She pointed to her sketch. It looked like Jud, all right, but the boy in the sketch wore an army uniform with a captain's bars.

"Don't change it!" Jud begged. "It isn't me, it's him. See— he's smiling!"

Dr. Harris looked from the picture to Jud. "You must be twins!"

"We . . . were." Jud's head dropped, and he covered his eyes with his hands.

"His brother was killed on Okinawa," Kay whispered. "He told me all about it."

"But I didn't tell you he was army, not a marine like me. And that he was a captain!" Jud's eyes were still fixed on the floor. "That's why that sketch hits me so hard!"

Dr. Harris pulled up a chair, and Kay sat on her stool beside her easel. Between them they got Jud talking. The words poured out—the story of the county fair and the boy who was so close to him for a few hours and then the other times when their paths crossed.

"His eyes were glazed, sir, when I told him we were twins. He was gone." Jud looked at Kay's charcoal sketch. "You can see, sir, that isn't me. It's *happy,* like Harry! I don't think I've smiled since he died. Ever since Okinawa I've gone around in a black cloud, because I was too late. I didn't tell him in time, and he died, not knowing we were twins."

Whatever Dr. Harris felt as a doctor, as a practical scientist his words showed his concern for the boy. "Now, wait a minute, Jud!" he said. "Why do you think, when Miss Olsen looked at *you*, she saw Harry? Even to the captain's bars? Don't you know that twins are different, hard to separate?"

Kay Olsen looked at the doctor, her eyes wet. Jud's outstretched hand clutched the doctor. "You mean he's . . . here; he's telling her? Is this his way of telling *me?*"

"Who knows?" said Dr. Harris wisely. "You didn't tell Miss Olsen that your twin was army or that he was a captain, but she saw! He guided her hand, Jud. I think Harry got your message, and this is his way of telling you."

Through a series of remarkable coincidences we were able to authenticate this story and locate the doctor's son, Derek T. Harris, of Newport Beach, California. He was in service at the time in Europe, but his wife and stepmother were present at the U.S.O. Club and heard Jud's story. Dr. Harris, a popular speaker, had told it frequently at various affairs until he went to South Africa. His son wrote to us:

> Father died there several years ago after having delivered a Zulu baby. It was a difficult breach birth, which was too strenuous for his heart. The Catholic priest, who was present at the time, wrote me a lovely letter and said that he died with a smile on his face.
>
> Prior to his death, I received what turned out to be my father's last letter, written at a small Catholic mission hospital in Zululand. The letter in itself was not unusual, but after reading it, my wife made the positive statement that my father was going to die soon. Only a week or so later, I received the letter about my father's death from the priest.

The Crail Twins

Near midnight on Christmas Eve, 1877, in a small frame house in a midwestern prairie town, two boys were born about an hour apart. They grew up to become lawyers and shared the same office for years. Both had active political careers. Charlie became the well-known Judge Charles S. Crail, of the Municipal Court in Los Angeles, and Joe was Congressman Joseph Crail. Bedeviling their teachers and classmates was their favorite sport in school, but occasionally their completely innocent "tricks" would backfire.

One such misadventure occurred during a Latin test in high school, when they had to translate a passage from Virgil. The papers they turned in were identical to the last word!

The teacher was a bulldozer of a woman whose voice made the Latin class resound like a marble quarry, the sentences all carved in stone. As she handed back the papers, she announced that the Crail twins were in disgrace.

"They cheated!" she bellowed. "Word for word alike!"

The twins were speechless for a moment, then they blurted out, "We didn't cheat! We're twins!"

The teacher's eyes blazed. "Don't I know that!" she roared. "But that's no excuse for copying!"

Flushed and stammering with resentment, the twins tried to protest. "What we mean is," said one, "twins do the same things and think the same thoughts—that's why the papers are the same."

"If you hadn't been sitting side by side, they wouldn't be!"

When they still protested, she put them on opposite sides of the room with a passage from the *Aeneid* to translate.

The twins repeated the test in silence, separated by the whole class. Again the papers were identical.

That proved nothing to the militant teacher. "Tomorrow," she said, "I'll give you another test, and the principal will help! You play your tricks before the principal, and you'll be expelled!"

The boys trudged home, miserable and depressed, then spent long hours that night reviewing Latin.

Next day there was great excitement throughout the school as the principal joined forces with the teacher. He took Joe by the collar. "You come into my office, Charlie!" He sounded even more stern than the teacher. "Joe will stay here." It was not a moment to point out to him that he had mixed their names.

Charlie felt abandoned without his twin. Shame and despair were emotions that had never swamped him before. Now the whole school thought they were cheating. The teacher brought him the new test paper and told him to get busy. This one was much more difficult. Charlie sat for nearly fifteen minutes just staring at it. The teacher, watching him, pounced again.

"Why don't you get busy?"

"I can't. I'm not ready." Charlie's voice conveyed all the misery he felt. Embarrassed and confused, he could not explain even to himself the paralysis that gripped him. "It seemed to me," he said, recalling it years later, "that there was some wheel in my brain which was not ticking in its accustomed rhythm."

After another long pause and more heckling from the teacher, the principal entered. He asked the teacher for his copy of the test! Joe (he said "Charlie") had been idly waiting in his office because the principal had been interrupted by someone.

Now, at last, they took the test together, Charlie (Joe) in the principal's office and Joe (Charlie) in the classroom. And this time all the wheels in both brains functioned normally.

At the end both boys were led into the principal's office. He was puzzled but not angry. "Boys," he said, "your Latin papers are identical again. The same words, the same syntax, the same grammar—and queerest of all, the same mistakes!"

The principal shook his head, but he was wise enough to say nothing more about a mystery he didn't understand.[1]

Such rapport is not enjoyed by all twins. There are some, indeed, who seem to hate and fear their twinship, who feel that living with another self robs them of their identity. One of the best illustrations of such a case is to be found in a fascinating book by R. E. L. Masters and his wife, Jean Houston, to whom we are indebted for the following, only substituting the names Barbara and Betty for their numbered examples:

> During their childhood the mother of these girls had done everything she could to make one sister literally indistinguishable from the other. The twin sisters were given identical clothing, identical haircuts, and compelled to engage in all the same activities together. So successful was the mother that she herself often could not tell one child from the other.
>
> By the time the girls were thirteen years old each deeply resented the other. Each wanted to be "a real individual, not just one half of a Siamese-twin team." The effect of this resentment, as the two grew older, was for each to differentiate herself as totally as possible from the other. . . .
>
> By the time they were thirty, one sister had become a physician and the other was an *avant garde* painter. They were still strongly antagonistic, quarreled heatedly over the most trivial matters and continued to dress and to wear their hair in very different styles. Even so, and although both denied it, the resemblance between them was considerable.

The authors, master researchers in their field, state that in spite of their hostility the twins saw each other now and then. Barbara, the doctor, had become interested in a group experiment with hallucinogenic drugs under psychiatric supervision, using the drug LSD as a means of penetrating into the psyche. The next time she met Betty, she persuaded her to join her as a cosubject in the group session. The results astounded everyone, including the twins:

> For the first hour or two of the session, the pair kept up their customary bickering. Then they became absorbed in their altered sense perceptions and images, and soon began comparing notes. To their astonishment each was experiencing almost the same changes of perception and the same images experienced by the other. They repeatedly inquired of the three other subjects in the room what those subjects were experiencing; and found, somewhat to their dismay, that the others were having quite different and highly individualized experiences.
>
> The twins also discovered that they were . . . finding the same things funny or sad for the same reasons, and drawing similar conclusions about their co-subjects. They went on comparing notes for some time, beginning to enjoy their "inexplicable mutuality," until a man in the room complained that they should keep their "Gemini perceptions" to themselves and asked, "Christ, don't either of you exist apart from the other one?" He added that the twins looked to him "like one person with two heads and four legs."
>
> These remarks had a strong effect on the twins, who reacted by intensely contemplating one another for a long time. At first they giggled at one another nervously, but then became pensive and finally appeared to be in a profound, almost trance-like sort of communion. It was while in this "empathic" state, they said later, that they had discovered themselves to be "essentially the same person." Each woman proclaimed herself to be "variations on my twin," but declared that the "overlapping of identities" no longer was a source of discomfort.
>
> The effect of this experience was to make the sisters "great friends" —and so they have remained for more than two years. At a time when one sister was going on a trip, she solicitiously urged a family friend "to take care of my other self"—something she "could never possibly have said" previous to the LSD session.

Among the strangest of the shared synesthesia of Barbara and Betty were "seeing the sounds" in reacting to the same piece of music, and when looking at a painting, they both exclaimed that they could "taste the color red!" They felt great delight in their restored mutuality and understanding.[2]

The Eckhardt Twins

One of the most spectacular sets of twins in the United States is little known outside magicians' groups. The story is told in *Genii, the Conjurer's Magazine* (April, 1962) by George Boston, former assistant to Blackstone and to both of the Thurston brothers.

The Eckhardt twins, John and Robert, were born in Baltimore on August 27, 1910. "At Johnny's birth," wrote Boston,

> his mother had twins. One baby the proper length and the other about half as long. Rob, Johnny's brother, matured into a full-sized man. Johnny is built as you and I but everything was pushed upwards. From the top of his head to about his elbows he is the same as his brother Rob. Then EVERYTHING STOPS. We hope he won't mind this description of him. Oh, yes, he's very much alive and very active in business with his brother. He is a familiar sight on the streets of Baltimore.

The boys grew from a single cell, but something happened in the womb to halt John's development. Nevertheless, he lived, and as the boys began to grow up, it was obvious that what John lacked in body he made up for in personality and blithe spirit. His nature was so remarkable that it transcended his handicap. He read widely, was an accomplished musician, and even became a race-car driver. Most amazing of all was his ability in team sports. He played baseball, for instance, standing on one hand, batting with the other, and he ran bases using his arms for legs. He was one of the best catchers on the team.

Those who remember Bob Ripley's "Believe It or Not" cartoons may recall one in which John was featured. Ripley later billed him as "Johnny Eck, the Half Boy" and exhibited him at the Chicago Century of Progress in 1933 in his Believe It or Not Odditorium.

"What can you do that I can't except tread water?" Johnny would joke. High-spirited, good company wherever he was, Johnny made one forget his body in enjoyment of his amazing many-faceted personality. He was a clever magician, a Punch-and-Judy operator, and a bandleader of more than ordinary skill.

While making the circuit in show business, Johnny inevitably met a popular magician of the times, Rajah Raboid. A fantastic scheme was concocted. Magicians had long featured a trick in which they "sawed" a girl in two. It was a thrilling bit of hocus-pocus, always enjoyed by the audience and relieved by the appearance of the girl in one piece at the end. Enlisting the help of Robert, Johnny's twin, the great magician made the trick seem an actuality.

The act was properly billed, and the theater was packed. The master magician was never better. The trick was one of the greatest illusions of all time, but it was far too real. Robert Eckhardt walked on stage and got into the "sawing-in-half box" with his head protruding from one end, his feet from the other. The magician took up a big saw and proceeded to cut the box in half.

When the halves were separated, the upper half of the body—in this case, Johnny—was removed and carried to the footlights on a large glass plate, talking and laughing for all he was worth. Gruesome, fantastic, and a real shocker! But at this point the audience screamed and bolted for the doors. The stampede of so many hysterical people inevitably caused trouble—and a few lawsuits.

Actually, the magician might have kept the act on the road if it had not been for his concern about Johnny's welfare. The lad had to be kept entirely hidden while traveling and especially in the towns where the act was billed. All the outdoor activities he loved such as riding, swimming, and driving would have to be sacrificed—as well as his own orchestra, perhaps his favorite of all. In addition, the magician was troubled about the traumatic effect such secrecy might have on the boy. So the act was shelved, thus ending what may well have been the most amazing magical illusion ever staged.

The twins grew up and went into partnership as the Eckhardt Brothers, renting theatrical equipment for magicians and other shows. It is a logical business for Johnny, for he is able to work with the people he loves and who love him in return.

Somehow Johnny seems to be a striking example of what Lord Byron meant when he said,

> All who joy would win
> Must share it—happiness was born a twin.

How Identical Are Identicals?

For a long time identical twins were believed to be identical to a ridiculous degree. In early German folklore it was said that identical

twins had the same number of hairs on their heads, though no
mathematician is quoted as having made the count! Still, everyone
believed that such a thing was possible, and these beliefs have a way
of persisting today, even after scientists entered the picture to prove
that in various ways identical twins were not identical.

Take the matter of fingerprints, for example. An FBI authority on
this subject stated that no two people in the world have identical
fingerprints, although identicals may be very close.

And no less an authority on twins than the late Horatio Hackett
Newman, University of Chicago biologist, had to battle more than
folklore to prove that in this detail, identicals were not alike.

Around 1940, when Newman had retired to Clearwater, Florida,
there appeared in print a story called "The Dark Mirror" by Vladimir
Posner. The whole plot hinged on identical twins with identical
fingerprints, and the author named Dr. Newman as his authority.

"When I read this rather second-grade story, I was mildly annoyed," Dr. Newman stated at the time. But instead of writing
directly to the publishers, he was moved merely to write an open
letter for publication in the local Clearwater *Sun*. In this he reiterated
statements he had made in his authoritative books to the effect that
he had never seen any prints that were so much alike that a good
fingerprint expert could not easily find differences.[3]

The first indication of trouble ahead was the announcement in
Time magazine that a film company was shooting a new picture
entitled *The Dark Mirror,* in which a famous actress was to star as
the twins and a very popular actor was the leading man.

A few days later Dr. Newman received by registered mail a legal
document containing two pages of the script involving court testimony
in which the professor was cited as authority that the fingerprints of
identical twins are sometimes identical. He was requested to sign this
document in duplicate before a notary, giving the producers the right
to use Dr. Newman's name in the way indicated in the script.

Of course, the flabbergasted professor refused to sign any such
document and wrote the producers that he regarded the use of his
name as an impertinence.

"I thought this would be the end of the episode so far as I was
concerned," he said, "but far from it!"

The climax came a few days later when a well-known writer telephoned him from Atlanta. He had adapted the story for the movies

and was on the spot. The producers had spent a large sum of money on film rights, settings, and high salaries for cast and technicians, and could the kindly professor offer any suggestions that might salvage the picture?

Dr. Newman could think of nothing helpful unless they cut out the fingerprint situation, but that would destroy the plot. Finally convinced, the screenwriter apologized. He threw all the blame on Vladimir Posner. The man was an Austrian refugee, he said, and had assured everyone that he had read all Newman's publications about twins and was on safe ground scientifically. Unfortunately, as soon as Posner was paid for the film rights, he disappeared, and it was assumed he had returned to Europe.

Law officers are often thwarted and even deliberately baited by twins with criminal inclinations. In the following case of typical mischief, Lloyd and Leon Longley turned identical twinship into a small but profitable racket. They were almost indistinguishable in appearance, voice, and mannerisms, even to their small, neat signature—L. Longley. Over the years they had worked up quite a business preying on merchants who unsuspectingly cashed modest checks.

So long as their twinship was secret, they had it made. Lloyd—or Leon—went on their "collection route" alone while the other twin socialized among respectable people in another area. If the rubber-check artist was caught, all he had to do was to use his brother's carefully established alibis while the latter lay low. Or occasionally, perhaps bored by dull routine, the twin would appear, and store-keepers would play the game of pick-the-twin in baffled anger.

But one day in Milwaukee Leon tried this stunt once too often. Lloyd was arrested, and officers had had their fill of the pair. They called in John F. Tyrrell, a courtly old gentleman who for more than fifty years had been testifying in court as a document detective. Tyrrell was given a sampling of checks signed L. Longley, and because of his report both twins were arrested.

The Longley twins were tried separately and sent to separate prisons. The judge reasoned that twins who wrote, talked, looked, and put on the same act alike would be too hard to handle in a single penal institution.[4]

2 WHAT MAKES A TWIN?

What determines the number of children conceived during any one pregnancy? If several, are they conceived at the same time or days apart? Do multiples run in families? Why are some twins identical in appearance, and others totally unlike? Is there an intermediate type of twin between look-alikes and unlikes? Are there twin-within-a-twin individuals—singly born? Can a boy-girl pair still be "identicals"? Can a woman take the new fertility drugs without danger of having her womb crowded with multiples?

These are a few of the questions we will attempt to answer in this book.

The marvels of pregnancy are many—not the least being the extraordinary variation in the ages at which it can occur. There are cases of twins born to child-mothers of thirteen and even of pregnancy before menstruation. Girls have menstruated at three years, have become grandmothers before twenty-one, and women in their sixties have conceived.[1]

The youngest set of parents known is a boy and girl of the Hsi family in Amoy, China, who on January 8, 1910, became the parents of a normal baby boy. The father was nine, the mother eight. The youngest female known to have conceived and borne a child is a five-year-old Peruvian Indian girl who gave birth to a healthy baby by cesarean section in 1939. No record is available on the very youngest to have twins.[2]

14

The Miracle of Human Cells

The most important cells in our bodies that are involved in the birth process are the sperm cells in the male and the egg cells in the female. In both sexes they are produced in dual organs called the gonads, from which they are expelled through ducts. In males these ducts carry sperm from the testes outside the body through the process of ejaculation. In females the reproductive cells remain much longer within the body, and the process is complex.

"It seems beyond comprehension," said the late Herman J. Muller, who received the 1946 Nobel Prize in physiology and medicine, "that a single cell contains within itself the entire machinery to make a baby shape itself and grow . . . especially when you remember that this cell is so small that if we could collect all such cells now existing in the world, we could pack them into a one-gallon pitcher!"

And don't forget that through doubling and redoubling, this cell can become twins or even quints!

When your baby girl is born, all the eggs that her ovaries will ever release, and far more, are already inside her body, although they are in potential, undeveloped form. There are probably half a million of them waiting in her tiny ovaries to divide. These later cell divisions will occur after she reaches puberty, although probably not more than four hundred of the half million will ever attain the stage at which they could be fertilized.

At adolescence the sex hormones begin to be stimulated by the tiny pituitary gland at the base of the brain. FSH (follicle-stimulating hormone) is secreted by both males and females, although its purpose in the male is still not perfectly understood. Its known purpose in the female menstrual cycle is to cause the eggs to mature—usually one per month—during the approximately thirty years of a woman's fertile life.

In a recent scientific breakthrough it has become possible to measure the level of FSH in the blood. That level, which is thought to be an inherited trait, presumably varies among individuals and races, and it may affect twin production. Its level is high in certain African tribes noted for twin births. FSH is also an active ingredient in fertility drugs. Now that it can be measured, doctors should be able to prevent the conception of more than one baby in those women who require such drugs.

Ordinary body cells divide into two equal parts in a process called *mitosis*. But the sex cells are differently made to permit the fertilized ovum to contain an equal number of characteristics from each parent. Here a still more complicated process called *meiosis* is required.

The ovum, or egg, is the largest of all human cells yet is just barely visible to the eye as a tiny speck. Its beginning was even more minute. It was then an oocyte, the undeveloped ovum. In this more complex cell division, unequal, smaller sister-cells are extruded from it, and from each other, into a "first polar body" and "second polar bodies." This final division occurs just before fertilization by the male sperm, when this new female cell ruptures from its follicle and travels down the fallopian tube, or oviduct, toward the womb.

Now there are two possibilities. Either it dies in a day or two and is discharged in the menstrual blood, or if sexual intercourse takes place during this brief period, it may be fertilized by a male cell, or sperm, in the semen.

Perhaps the lowly frog should receive a special citation from geneticists, since it was from these creatures that a basic fact of life was learned. Using the primitive microscope of the 1600's, early researchers had observed spermatozoa without being sure of their part in the life cycle. But late in the eighteenth century the Abbé Lazzaro Spallanzani made tight silk pantlets for his male frogs and let them swim above female eggs in his tanks. Not until he removed the panties did the eggs become tadpoles!

Biological Processes Affecting Twinship

How does it happen that more than one infant is sometimes conceived at a time? This can occur through two entirely different biological processes. The two processes result in the two different types of twins, "identical" and "fraternal"—"one egg" and "two egg"—or as scientists call them, MZ and DZ, monozygotic and dizygotic, the zygote being the fertilized ovum, or egg.

Statistics on twins are valueless unless it is known which type they are.

But just what are identical twins? They are not necessarily—or always—twins who look alike. They result only if, after intercourse, the cell (fertilized by a single sperm) divides in two. But some women release two eggs at times instead of one. If both these eggs are fertilized by two different sperm, then fraternal, or unlike, twins may result.

One-egg, or identical, twins, since they arise from division of a single cell, have the same genes from both the father and the mother, and of course belong to the same sex (except for one very rare abnormality to be discussed later). Some geneticists believe one-egg twinning itself is an inherited abnormality—an arrest in development occurring very early in embryonic life before tissue differentiation has begun.

Two-egg, or fraternal, twins may be as unlike as ordinary brothers and sisters, or they may be so alike that they are mistakenly thought to be identical. *They may, in fact, in extraordinary cases even have different fathers,* as has been proved by blood tests in court. But don't leap to such wildly improbable suspicions from mere unlikeness!

Some twins are so identical that, like Kae and Rae Taylor of the Nitty Gritty Dirt Band, they can even wear each other's contact lenses. But if heredity were the only factor, there obviously could never be differences.

Dr. H. H. Newman—himself a twin and one of the first to research the subject, at the University of Chicago in the 1930's—mentioned an unusual pair of one-egg girls. In early life they could hardly be told apart, yet one became a hunchbacked invalid while the other remained healthy. Another pair of boys were "identical" genetically, though one grew six inches taller and twenty-three pounds heavier. Here diabetes insipidus had depressed growth in one twin.

"It is the existence of such one-egg twins as these which makes the term 'identical twin' inappropriate for one-egg twins," Newman observed.

In his day many of the tests now available were unknown, but even today mistakes can occur. Actually the term "identical" refers *only to heredity,* since appearance, health, and disposition may differ widely. Occasional pairs of two-egg twins are found to be almost as similar as some of the less-alike identicals.

Mirror-Image Twins

About one in every three pairs of twins will be identicals, and among identicals there can be infrequently a still stranger event— "mirror-image" twins. This condition is not well understood but may result when egg-splitting is delayed until probably the seventh day. Some geneticists say it is a matter of pure chance. Here the forehead curls turn in opposite directions, while birthmarks, the large eye, and the prominent tooth appear on opposite sides of each twin's face. Occasionally even the heart, appendix, and other internal organs can be on different sides of the body.

Dr. Newman had an interesting theory here. With these rare cases of organ-reversals he suspected that when they occurred with single births, the infant had started life as a twin, and the other had failed to develop in the womb. Other scientists disagree and blame recessive genes. Newman noted mirror-imaging occasionally in unlike twins— which by his theory would suggest that a third fetus, identical to one of the living twins, might have been absorbed before birth.

Occasionally twins marry twins and produce more twins.

The Rubin case is famous among geneticists. In 1937 identical twin brothers, Benjamin and Hyman Rubin in Great Neck, New York, married identical twin girls, Sylvia and Ruth Reisman. From the beginning they shared the same home. One couple had identical twin girls, the other a single boy, born four days later. They raised the children like brothers and sisters, which they actually were genetically.

"Are the two babies of one couple the double first cousins," asked Newman, "or the sisters of the single baby of the other couple?"

Because each set of parents had identical genes, the three children were as similar as if they belonged to one father and mother. They did not, in fact, know the difference until they were about ten. Later in the book we will mention more such marriages.

Can There Be an Intermediate Class of Twins?

"Our twin boys are so alike!" said a mother of twins to us. "The doctors have made test after test and still insist they are fraternals, not identicals. How can this be? Really, they are much more alike than my sister's identicals! I wonder if there can't be an in-between class of twins that doctors don't recognize yet."

This idea has been considered by geneticists for years. Some of them have suggested that occasionally eggs might divide in the oocyte stage *before fertilization* and then be fertilized by different sperm. In this case the twins would be half identical, with the same genes from the mother and different ones from the father. Other scientists suggest that such twins might come from fertilization of two cells from a single ovum by a two-headed sperm. (Such sperm are often but not always attributable to alcohol or syphilis.)

In Baltimore in 1953 Dr. George W. Corner examined a seventeen-day-old twin embryo. They were identified as identical by Dr. Chester H. Heuser, who said they gave indisputable proof that a one-egg twin, or identical, can actually develop in this intermediate way—that is, by the formation inside a single blastocyst (the germinal vesicle of the ovum) of two areas, each of which then becomes a separate embryo.[3]

But Dr. M. G. Bulmer in his recent work *The Biology of Twinning in Man* discusses the remarkable recent discovery of "mosaic" individuals. He believes instead that although the mechanism for a third or intermediate type of twin does exist in man, it will actually result in the twin-within-a-twin single individual.[4] An explanation of the phenomenon appears in the following chapter.

Additional Factors That Result in Twins

Other subtle factors can also cause twinning. Cutting down oxygen supply causes fish eggs to split, and keeping them at low temperature for an hour produces double abnormalities. Thus one cause of twinning, especially imperfect twinning, may be any temporary stoppage of development at a critical stage.

Possibly temperature also enters into one distinction between male and female reproductive cells. In man and some animals the male cells—being outside the abdominal region in the testicles—are, of course, somewhat cooler than the mother's within the ovaries. During pregnancy her abdomen and breasts become hotter than the rest of her body. It is also known that during excessive summer heat fertility declines.

Surprisingly enough, one entirely modern cause of twinning, though probably only occasional, is the pill.

While a woman is taking the pill, her pituitary stores FSH. When pill-taking ceases, this FSH is excreted from the pituitary gland. It may be an unusually large amount at first because of the storage. This larger amount may stimulate more than one ovum, and hence multiple ovulation may occur. If pregnancy follows, *fraternal* twins, triplets, and other multiples may result.

Blood transfusions have also been suspected as a possible cause, the mother receiving a twinning factor from a donor.

Because sperm can be accumulated and frozen, supposedly barren couples have been able by artificial insemination of the husband's own sperm to have children who are really their own—both singletons and twins. The problem here is usually that the husband's ejaculate is deficient in the number of motile sperm, but by accumulating the sperm from a number of separate ejaculations and then freezing it, the original method of using an anonymous donor is not needed. About ten thousand such conceptions occur annually in the United States.

The Riddle of Identical Twins

The riddle of which twin is which is an ancient one. Even a bloodhound can seldom tell identical twins apart. Since the blood group antigens and the basic biochemical peculiarities, including sweat, are the same for identical twins, the poor hounds usually sniff their heads off to no purpose. Perhaps the family pet learns to tell Jim from Joe, but police dogs need special training to acquaint them with the subtle distinction between the scents.

A second riddle, surprisingly enough, is to determine whether a pair of twins is identical or fraternal. Modern geneticists find this no simple task and no longer accept as conclusive the reports from midwives or even from doctors. Instead, they use correlation tests—identical blood type, hair, eye color, near-identical fingerprints, and other body measurements taken with calipers.

Not even a single placenta, or afterbirth, is proof—as was once supposed—for the placentas of fraternal twins can fuse if the two fertilized eggs reached the womb about the same time and adhered close together upon it. The two eggs may have come from one or both ovaries.

With identicals the sooner the egg splits into two, the more closely the pair will resemble each other. If the cell division takes place very early, each embryo will have its own birth-robe (outer bag, or chorion), water sac (inner bag, or amnion holding the fluid), afterbirth (placenta), and its own navel string, or umbilical cord.

Very rarely does the whole bag still cover the baby when it arrives. In the Highlands of Scotland they say such a child was "born with a caul" and has "the sight" (is psychic). They call this torn membrane the holy hood or hallihoo and believe it has magical and medical powers. Sometimes the midwife sells it as a charm against drowning or to develop psychic gifts.

In multiple births separate sacs give more safety to the infants, for there can be complications if through late egg-splitting, twins grow within the same outer bag. And if they also share the same water sac, there is danger of injury from cramping or from tangling of the cords.

A major reason why fraternal twins run in families is that daughters seem to inherit their mothers' tendency to produce two eggs. Environment may also have an effect, for country life and a colder climate seem to favor two-egg twinning.

Geneticists argue as to whether the tendency to bear identicals is inherited or results from chance, yet identicals are sometimes found in families where only the father was identical. This raises the possibility that egg-splitting may derive from either parent.

The matter was discussed by Professor Luigi Gedda, of the prestigious Twin Institute in Rome, who has more than ten thousand twin cases computerized. He says: ". . . both mother and father may carry the trait responsible for both MZ and DZ twinning, the maternal contribution being more relevant. . . . [She] may have inherited it through her father as well as through her mother (or even through both)."[5]

Percentage Chances of Having Twins

About eleven mothers out of one thousand in the United States will have twins. Who these mothers will be depends on four factors: the woman's age, her race, her heredity, and the number of children she already has. Her chances of a multiple birth drop sharply if for her, one or more of these four factors say, "Twins unlikely!"

Negro women in their thirties have the highest percentage of twins, Orientals the lowest. A teen-aged white mother pregnant for the first time has only six chances in one thousand of having twins. But for all races the chance increases following each pregnancy until fertility begins to decline at about forty.

However, this applies only to fraternal, two-egg twins. The reason is that the younger the woman, the less apt she is to release two eggs at a time. Now that girls are marrying so early, the ratio of fraternals to identicals is dropping. If you are forty and white, your chance of having fraternal twins is four times greater than when you were twenty. (For nonwhites the peak age comes between thirty and thirty-four rather than thirty-five and thirty-nine.)

The number of multiple births in the United States also varies greatly from state to state, possibly because in older, rural areas there is more intermarriage. Thus Kentucky has almost twice as many twins as Nevada—1 in 66.8 births as against 1 in 123.7.[6]

Recent figures give the following incidence of twins: United States white, 1 in 85–90; United States Negro, 1 in 76; African Negro, 1 in 50; Oriental, 1 out of 152. In Europe figures vary from 1 in 62 in Denmark to 1 in 111 in Spain, suggesting that northern races have more twins than Mediterranean stock. This racial or ethnic difference applies to *fraternals only*. The frequency of *identicals* is almost the same worldwide at about 3.5 per 1,000. Probably 40 percent of like-sexed twins are identicals.

But statistics in countries where twins are called "unlucky" are not always reliable, since except for hospital births the data may be suppressed. Even in the United States the census does not count early miscarriages, cases where the fetus was absorbed, or anomalies born with a normal child. Sometimes infants born dead are not recorded. Most states require registration after twenty weeks of fetal life, but this requirement is sometimes evaded, and illegal abortions distort statistics still further.

About half of all fraternal twins are male-female combinations. No boy-girl pairs are look-alikes—although Shakespeare and other writers were fond of this plot.

Mothers who have had one set of twins have a higher chance of repeating the feat. In July, 1961, Mrs. Mary Pearson, of Jacksonville, Florida, had her seventh set of twins. Yet the odds against having more than three consecutive sets is said to be about ten million to one![7]

A Canadian family, however, the Tremblays (pictured in this book), had six sets in eight years, and a Sicilian mother bore eleven sets in eleven years, all fraternals. Her last pair arrived in 1947; not all survived.

The odds against four generations in a row having twins are about

57,309 to 1, but in July, 1963, Mrs. Hazel Moore of Petersburg, Virginia, had twin girls. She is a twin herself, and so were her mother and grandmother.[8]

Cases of fabulous fertility have been recorded over the centuries. Dr. Ambroise Paré, renowned sixteenth-century surgeon, reported on one mother, Mme. de Maldemeure, wife of the Lord of Seaux near Chambellay, France. She had twenty-one children in six years, the number increasing by exact progression: one at her first confinement, then twins, triplets, quadruplets, and quints. She died when she bore six! The case was well known, since the family was prominent among the nobility.

A modern mother in Cleveland, Ohio, married three times, had not only seven pairs of twins, but five sets of triplets and three of quads.

But the most phenomenal multiples are probably two Russian cases in the last century. In 1853 a peasant named Kirilow, aged seventy, was presented to the Empress of Russia. He had fathered sixty-six children, all multiple births. His first wife had had quads four times, triplets seven times, and twins three times. His second wife had had triplets seven times also, and twins once.

Another Russian had eighty-seven children, of whom eighty-four lived. This man was Fedor Vassilet. His first wife was so renowned for her fertility that she, too, was presented at court under Czar Alexander II. She bore sixty-nine children: sixteen pairs of twins, seven sets of triplets, and four sets of quads before she died in 1872. Her husband's second wife had two sets of triplets and six pairs of twins. (Some authorities attribute the sixty-nine children, in the same combinations, to a Mrs. Bernard Scheinberg, of Austria, but our reference is earlier, and we believe it is correct.[9])

Since nature does not always carry through what she began, what started out as a twin may end as a single birth. So anyone may have twins in his ancestry without knowing it. *Perhaps you yourself began life in the womb as a twin and never knew it!*

What enormous resourcefulness must be developed by these mothers of amazing multiples! This can have its humorous side.

Back in the 1920's in Laporte, Indiana, a Mrs. Frank Scott boarded a streetcar and proffered a nickel as fare for herself and her thirteen children. The conductor refused.

"Why not?" she demanded. "They are all mine, and all under five,

so they ride free!" To prove it she pulled the family Bible from a
capacious bag and pointed to their birth record.

Abel and Abner were six months old, and Archer, Austen, and
Ashbel, the oldest triplets, were four and a half. In less than five years
she had three sets of triplets and two pairs of twins.[10]

Twins in the Animal Kingdom

In the very early stages of embryonic life only an expert can distinguish between fish, turtle, calf, and man—showing the close relationship among living things. But by the eighth week the human fetus
resembles a tiny infant only an inch long.

With polar bears twins are usual. Marmoset monkeys usually have
two-egg twins, but apes normally have single births. Sheep and goats
have twins and triplets fairly often. Early in the nineteenth century
the Italian naturalist Bassi—himself a twin—greatly increased the
number of twins among his sheep by careful selection. He found that
the most (and finest) twins came from rams and ewes not too young,
of good size, proven record, and above all, well fed. Here, as with
human twins, good nutrition was vital. Twin ewes and their daughters
also had their twins with greater ease.[11]

The twinning rate also varies among the different breeds of domes-
tic animals. One breed of cows has twins perhaps once in fifty times,
another once in twenty. A Holstein in a Clarksburg, West Virginia,
dairy fantastically produced six calves at once—all perfect.

Usually animal multiples are believed to come from separate eggs,
but since two-headed animals occasionally occur, some must develop
from a single egg. One species, the little nine-banded scaly armadillo
of Texas, invariably produces four young, all from a single egg en-
cased in a single membrane, but other types of armadillos may occasionally discharge two eggs at once like a human mother.

Dr. Kurt Benirschke, geneticist at the University of California's San
Diego School of Medicine, says: "This nine-banded armadillo has a
magnificent placenta! It is so perfect an organ for nourishing her little
quadruplets that in thousands of births I have never seen an abnormal offspring."

If only the human placenta were anywhere near as perfect, adds
Dr. Benirschke, who was head pathologist at Boston's Lying-In
Hospital for a decade, multiple births among women would be enor-
mously safer.

3 INGENIOUS GEMINATION—
THE HEREDITY STORY

Heredity, says the old joke, is what a man believes in until his son begins to act like a fool. The argument as to whether heredity or environment, nature or nurture, dominates has raged for many years.

Apparently, although both are important, heredity is one lap ahead. It provides the recipe, says one writer, and no amount of tenderizer can turn pot roast into filet mignon.

In the prudish days beginning this century a popular rhyming query, "Where did you come from, baby dear?" was answered in kind, "Out of the everywhere into the here!" But the science of genetics had scarcely come out of the everywhere itself in that sentimental era.

Today the enormously complex jigsaw is being mastered bit by bit, as scientists all over the world contribute the results of their research. Many small areas make up the total picture, and sometimes a new test flatly contradicts previously accepted beliefs.

The Role of Chromosomes

The most momentous gift you will ever receive is your own forty-six chromosomes—twenty-three from each parent. Which twenty-three out of each parent's own forty-six you will receive is apparently pure chance—but on that chance a great part of your life history will depend.

The ovum, small though it is, is still enormously larger than the infinitesimal sperm, for the ovum must contain the food to sustain itself through egg-splitting before the placenta is formed. But egg and sperm each contribute exactly half of our hereditary factors. The nucleus of the cell is the control center containing the chromosomes, on which lie the strings of tiny genes. A single human cell is estimated to contain about a million genes—an awesome glimpse into the world of the infinitely tiny.

The name "chromosome" (*chromo,* color; *soma,* body) arises because the protoplasm of the cell nucleus absorbs artificial coloring more readily for observation under the microscope. Surrounding it is the outer protoplasm, or cytoplasm. It is very likely that part of our inherited endowment lies in this cytoplasm around the nucleus. "Of this, however, we know virtually nothing, while we have a great deal of exact information about gene-controlled inheritance," says the venerable French biologist Jean Rostand.[1]

The chromosomes take food from the egg, then split themselves; and this process of multiplication and division goes on with both chromosomes and cells until the human (or animal) "pattern" is set.

Although people often say, "I'm one-fourth Chinese, Swedish," etc., this is inaccurate. No one can determine how many chromosomes from each race he has received. It varies even with nonidentical (fraternal) twins. Appearance proves nothing. The twin who looks most like his father may be more like his mother in talents and personality. With interracial marriages the one who looks most Oriental might easily have fewer Chinese genes. In years to come these questions may be answerable.

Chromosomal Disorders

From top to toe every cell of male and female bodies is different. Normally, a girl's two sex chromosomes are XX, whereas the boy's sex chromosomes have an X and a smaller Y.

But recently doctors have made a startling discovery. So far the oddity or exception has only been recorded with single births, but as more cases come in, some are certain to be found among identical male twins.

These are oddities of two types. Once in about one thousand births an extra X chromosome sneaks in, resulting in an XXY grouping in which the male tends toward the female and is unusually tall, often retarded, and sterile.

Then once in about every two thousand births an extra Y chromosome has been found that has made headlines in some vicious murder cases. This is an XYY male, the so-called supermale of which Richard Speck, the murderer of the eight Chicago nurses, is an example. Dr. Mary Telfer, a biochemist at the Elwyn Institute (Elwyn, Pennsylvania) who has made a study of such cases, estimates that whereas among tall men in general, one in eighty may have this Y chromosome, among criminals it rises to one in eleven. Since no one knows for certain how many men leading blameless lives may also be typed thus, the behavior patterns of XXY and XYY males cannot be precisely determined.

Those who have this imbalance are tall, slender, and vigorous. In the beginning it seemed that both types were mentally dull, but this has not proved true of the XYY. A survey among athletes, who often fulfill this description without criminal inclinations, is planned. This may put a damper on the excitement among criminal lawyers all too eager to get clients freed because of "chromosomal insanity."

Such a case was that of the "Jolly Green Giant" charged with the gruesome murder of a waitress in Queens, New York, in 1968. He was tracked down through the description of patrons of a tavern he frequented, who had given him that nickname because of his size (6' 6", 240 pounds) and his green haberdashery. At about the same time a man in Melbourne, Australia, accused of murder, was acquitted on grounds of insanity, and in Paris a defendant was given a frighteningly light sentence, based on this XYY abnormality. The Paris murder of a prostitute was similar to London's mysterious Jack the Ripper in the gaslight era. In view of these cases it is interesting that Richard Speck's lawyers did not use this defense after his murder of the eight nurses in Chicago.[2]

And that exceedingly rare combination, the boy-girl "identical twins" *from the same egg,* comes about if during egg-splitting there is a mix-up of the sex chromosomes, and one Y is dropped. Here, instead of a two-boy pair, one twin becomes an imperfect girl, unable to reproduce, like a freemartin calf, and possibly retarded. The other twin, who got the usual XY, is normal.

The authors recently viewed a slide of one of these rare boy-girl identicals. One child was a head taller than the other, but there was a strong resemblance. Unfortunately, we were unable to obtain a print of these twins, who live abroad.

Women are not immune to chromosomal disorders, although they are not subject to the one that, perhaps, relates to criminality in tall males. But they can have others that seriously affect their unborn children. And it has been research with identical twins that has helped doctors to pinpoint which diseases are due to heredity.

Nancy, a twenty-one-year-old mother whose mongoloid infant had died, went to Dr. Henry L. Nadler, a Chicago pediatrician who specializes in heredity counseling. There are two forms of mongolism —one hereditary, the second an accident that occurs perhaps once in eight hundred births. With identical twins, both are invariably afflicted.[3]

Dr. Nadler found no history of mongoloid retardation on either side, so he made a microscopic study of the chromosomes of both parents. In Nancy's he discovered the reason: A twenty-third strange formation marked her as a carrier. But Dr. Nadler said she still had a one-in-three chance of giving birth to a normal child. If she became pregnant again, a further test, amniocentesis, could determine the facts.

By this method a tiny sample of the amniotic fluid surrounding the fetus is taken from the womb. This is removed painlessly by a long needle during the fourteenth to sixteenth week of pregnancy. It will detect at least twenty-five genetic disorders and several other problems leading to defects such as mongolism.

If the sample proved abnormal, a therapeutic abortion would be suggested. So Nancy and her husband decided to try for another pregnancy, and fortunately a few months later the test revealed that they could expect a normal baby girl.

"Now we know it can be a controlled pregnancy, we're planning for still another child," Nancy said happily.

Some doctors believe that infrequent intercourse among older couples could be responsible for some mongolism, for these children are far more common with older mothers. They reason that the egg lives for only about forty-eight hours after ovulation, but sperm may remain alive in the cervix for several days. Thus a woman who has frequent marital relations will always have potent sperm available for fertilization, but otherwise an egg may already have deteriorated before a sperm reaches it. Accordingly, frequent relations may lessen the risk of mongoloids. The defect was probably rarer in the past, because two hundred years ago nearly half the women died before their thirty-fifth birthday.

Mysteries still remain, such as why having had one abnormal child increases the risk of having another by up to ten times. Strangest of all, why are more abnormal children born during certain months of the year? Conception during excessive summer heat may be one cause.

However, United States Government statistics show an annual occurrence of about 25,000 birth abnormalities that are due to an irregular number of chromosomes.

Most defects and malformations result from complex interactions. At the moment of conception the child's sex and some types of abnormalities are determined. But many other defects may arise from excessive exposure to X rays too early, perhaps before pregnancy was even suspected; from poor diet and certain drugs, including the hallucinogens; and from accidents before or during birth. The fact that the risk of malformations as well as mongolism rises with older mothers is probably both genetic and environmental. Some forms of dwarfism may stem from older fathers.

Thus, since multiple births do bring a higher chance of a defective child, if there have been abnormalities in the family line, a sample of fluid from the womb should always be taken. If diagnosed unfavorably, the parents might prefer to have a risky pregnancy terminated, since a long, tragic illness with enormous expense could divert funds and time from the other children, with little real benefit to the handicapped one.

For information about the birth-defects center nearest you, write to the National Foundation—March of Dimes, Medical Department, Box 2000, White Plains, New York 10602.

Some doctors are even attempting the extraordinarily delicate operation of removing the fetus from the womb. In one of these operations the baby would have died because of Rh blood incompatible with the mother's. After replacing the blood in the tiny fetus by transfusion, the doctors stayed with the mother for forty-eight hours.[4] "The uterus is a highly reactive organ," they said. "Once it is entered, some unknown mechanism starts it contracting, and the fetus is pushed out."

In this case they were successful, and the mother bore a healthy little girl. At other times a catheter is left in place in the abdomen of the fetus, so that transfusions may be repeated for weeks or even months. However, these dangerous fetal or at-birth transfusions may soon become largely avoidable. If the new gamma globulin RhoGAM is injected into the mother within seventy-two hours after the birth of her first child, she will not become sensitized to the baby's differing factors.

Human Blood Chimeras

An early mystery in the story of blood typing was revealed through a twin known as Mrs. McK., described in the *British Medical Journal* for July, 1953, as a "human blood chimera." To the ancients a chimera was a fabled animal with a lion's head, a serpent's tail, and a goat's body. This twenty-five-year-old Englishwoman was the first person found to have two blood types. She was classified as both O and A after giving a pint of blood.

Previously twin calves had been the only creatures known to have such an admixture. When a bull-and-heifer pair is born, the heifer is often a freemartin which cannot bear young or give milk. But just why this happens only among the ruminants (cattle, sheep, etc., with four-chambered stomachs), and not among the apes and mankind, has no final and plausible explanation at this point in time.

The mystery was complicated by the fact that Mrs. McK.'s twin brother had died in infancy. But later other women "blood chimeras" were found with living twins who could be typed. Specialists concluded there had been connections between the placental blood vessels of these twins, and they found that skin grafts between them would "take," as is usually the case with the male-female cattle twins. The earlier and rare successful grafts between human fraternals are now thought to have the same explanation.

Twin within a Twin

A very remarkable recent finding is the discovery of "mosaic" or whole-body chimeras in whom all the tissues (not just the blood) show two distinct cell lines which must have come from *two different sperm*.

A friend of ours who seems to be a twin within a twin writes us:

Have you gotten onto this whole new business of total twinning, i.e., such as myself and many others who are now thought to be actually two bodies in one, with two slightly different sets of genes, but not necessarily two personalities in the classic schizoid definition. I am not a schizoid by all known tests, but I *may be* what is called a "suppressed twin"—which is to say, two ID's in one, with two sets of reproductive cells with quite different chromosomal counts.

I had twin sisters but they died before birth. I have three teats; my mother had four, her mother had six, though all of us have only the normal two breasts.

These twin-within-a-twin individuals may have existed unsuspected within the human stream for centuries. They can be normal, even mentally brilliant, but in some cases may have noticeable peculiarities such as one blue and one brown eye.

One girl's body cells were equally divided between XY and XX. In addition, she had red cells of different blood groups. The typing of her parents' blood showed that the variation in eye color and blood groups came from her father, conception having been achieved through fertilization by *two* sperm instead of the usual single sperm. In her situation and others one sperm seemingly fertilized an ovum, and the other, one of the polar bodies (that is, cells separating at the time of the formation of the ovum, during meiosis).

During the process of fertilization in test tubes, occasional oocytes may have two nuclei, and sperm have also been observed to enter the second polar body and start development. The matter is speculative, since, naturally, it has not been seen within a living body.

With two-egg twins the blood circulation is almost never connected, but when it is, it probably gives rise to blood chimerism. With one-egg twins it becomes an extra hazard. One twin may bleed into the other, become anemic, and die; also the umbilical cords may twist.

In another case of a very abnormal XX/XY boy who did not live long, there were noticeable pigmented stripes on the skin which darkened in sunlight. Thus a mechanism for the supposed third type of twin may exist, but in man it probably leads to these mosaic individuals instead of to a pair of fetuses. Dr. Kurt Benirschke in his review of the subject states: "No rigid boundaries exist between the various types of twins, chimeras and mosaics."[5]

These complexities of genetic assessment make some of the questions that began our previous chapter superficial. When you realize that (very rarely) identicals occur who are of opposite sex, or that a single person may in himself be a "mosaic," you can no longer wonder why your own identical Alice-Aline are look-alikes while your sister's Ella-Ellen pair are so different!

Chimerism also exists in animals. It was long believed by cat breeders that "calico" cats with orange patches on black and white fur were always female, but recently several calico males have been found. One of the cats was a normal fertile male, but others had two-colored eyes or various sexual abnormalities.[6]

In an earlier case a very strange chicken was studied in the Department of Animal Genetics at the University of Illinois. Half of the chicken had the black and white stripes of the barred Plymouth Rock with the ordinary bare-shanked leg. But the other half displayed the handsome cream plumage of a Brahma, with its fluffy, heavily feathered shank on that side.

The Role of the Placenta

Although the idea may seem startling, babies are parasites, since they are foreign bodies within a host—the mother. Only the after-birth, or placenta (the spongy "pancake" in the womb through which the child receives its nourishment), prevents the baby's rejection as foreign matter by its mother's body. While normally no actual blood passes back and forth, glucose, oxygen, and amino acids reach the child by diffusion, and its wastes are passed back to the mother to be eliminated.

Thus until birth the placenta serves the child in the place of its lungs, kidneys, liver, intestines, and endocrine glands. It gives oxygen to the fetus, although it cannot filter out all viruses and may be contaminated by cigarettes or drugs. The placenta also makes needed hormones for the mother-host; without them she may abort.

In multiple pregnancies there is competition even within that supposedly safe place, the womb. The environment within the mother is not identical for "identicals." One fetus may be more crowded, receive less blood or immunity from the placenta, or become entangled in its own cord. Birth order and accidents at that time can also cause variations. Weight may vary considerably according to the place on the placenta where the cord is attached.

Of course, twins in themselves stretch the uterus, resulting in a larger placenta and an increased amount of amniotic fluid. For safety, twins should not add more than twenty-five pounds to the mother's weight, as against twenty for a singleton. By the eighth week cartilage begins to be replaced by bone cells in the embryo (Greek, meaning "to swell within"), and it is now called the fetus (Latin, meaning "young one"). At about the fourth month the fetal heart begins to beat.

Signs That Point to Twins

Mothers themselves seldom know that a "twinfant" is on the way. What are some of the signs? One of the most obvious is rapid increase in weight or size; also excessive heartburn, vomiting, and skin discolorations. When the doctor presses on the mother's abdomen, he may feel extra arms and legs or even two bony little heads. Although X rays are a positive indication, they may be harmful to the child if excessive exposure is given before the twenty-fourth week. Several new devices can be used much earlier and without risk— ultrasonics, telemetering, and thermography.

Ultrasonics, labeled by medical scientists at Columbia Presbyterian Medical Center as being a thousand times safer than X rays, was used there with pregnant mice in 1962. Similar to the navy's high-frequency sound waves for the detection of submarines, it lacks the clarity of X rays. But in scanning the uterus, it shows a clear outline of the fetus and multiple pregnancies, with total freedom from toxicity.

The telemetering device, perfected at Yale University, can detect the infant heartbeat by about the fourteenth week. Thermography, because of the higher temperature over the womb, can also reveal the facts with a special camera.

In spite of the hazards of pregnancy there seems no limit, at times, to what the uterus can endure. A Winchester, Kentucky, mother-to-be, accidentally shot in the abdomen, was rushed to the hospital three weeks before the birth was expected. The baby was saved by cesarean section, although the bullet had struck near his brain. It was removed with no damage.

The ancients had laws compelling cesareans to be performed on women who died during pregnancy. Had some infants not survived, the law would probably have been rescinded. Historic cases of near-miracle births mention safe arrivals to mothers gored by bulls or injured by cannon when they tagged behind the army as camp followers. A story from the merciless days of the Spanish Inquisition told of a pregnant woman who was hanged in 1551, only to have twins found beneath her body on the gallows.

Incredible as it seems, there have been recorded cases of childbirth where the mother remained asleep throughout.

Longevity of Twins

Although in the first month of life multiples have a death rate five to six times higher than singletons, this seems largely due to the handicap of premature birth. After this initial period is safely passed, their chances are about the same as for single births.

As for their longevity—a hereditary factor—it is also the same. "The way in which longevity is inherited is entirely unknown," says Jean Rostand. "But it obviously depends on the general organization of the body and consequently it must be controlled by a large number of genes." He quotes statistics showing that length of life has a relationship to our immediate forebears. The TIAL (total immediate ancestral longevity) is equal to the sum of the ages at death of the two parents and four grandparents. The higher our TIAL, the greater our chance of long life. The TIAL of a 100-year-old man cited was 599—93 being the shortest life of his close forebears.[7]

Some members of multiples have come close to equaling this. Fillmore, California, claimed the oldest twins in the United States when Mattie and Sarah Duckworth celebrated their ninety-eighth birthday on February 10, 1964. And three midwestern triplet sisters —Mesdames Ida Ellis, Ruth DeMoss, and Lee Farmer—enjoyed theirs at seventy-five over cheery cups of tea. They were born in rural Kentucky and kept warm in shoe boxes beside a potbellied stove. Both groups are pictured in this book.

The famous Coughlin triplets, Faith, Hope, and Charity, were born in 1867. Faith died at ninety-five, Hope at ninety-eight. The date of Charity's death is not known.

Obviously the greater mechanical and chemical load on the mother's body, crowding in the womb, tube pregnancies, and difficult presentation at birth increase the risks for mothers of multiples.

Because of this extra load on the mother's system, many twins are prematurely born. But it is little known that most of today's "preemies" owe their lives to the robust unorthodoxy of an obscure young obstetrician in the Paris of 1890.

When one of his first patients had a premature infant, Dr. Martin Couney determined to save it. Rigging up a crude incubator, he kept a twenty-four-hour watch and saved the child. Case after case came to him, but the excessive care made it unfeasible and costly.

Then an idea struck him—let the babies pay their own way! The public was already excited about his success. He would put them on display at fairs, and the fees collected could pay for the necessary care and treatment.[8]

His colleagues scorned such crude publicity but still sent him their "hopeless" cases. Crowds watched delightedly while the infants were fed, bathed, and diapered in the aquarium-like incubator. Germs must have been rampant on these occasions, yet baby after baby survived. Perhaps they thrived in the limelight like performing seals, as he toured with his little pets.

More than seven thousand infants owed their lives to an obstetrician who was not afraid to flout the ethics of his profession by the use of showmanship.

Twins Born Days Apart

Misfortunes and twins rarely come singly—but sometimes they do! In this parade of parallel and paradox it has even happened that twins have been born many days apart.

In 1965 a Yugoslavian mother had twin sons twenty-five days apart. Mrs. Janja Kralj, living in the little village of Bradac in Bosnia, gave birth to her son Nicola on August 14.

"What struck me was that my stomach was still large," she said. "But only when the pain for the second birth started did I realize that I was still with child!" When Miro appeared, he was twice as heavy as his brother, but both were healthy and made good progress.

Similar twins were also reported in Bengal, born forty-five days apart.

We have pictorial proof of one of these sets. An Associated Press wirephoto shows a beaming Australian mother holding babies alike as peas on either arm—born fifty-six days apart. It is impossible to tell from the picture which of these twins matured within the womb and which outside it. Denis Alan was born to Mrs. A. Goodwin, of Newton, Sydney, on December 16, 1952. His brother, David Bruce, did not arrive until February 10, 1953. (See photograph of these babies in this book.)

However, the record number of days between births seems to have occurred in 1846 in Strasbourg, France—a 137-day interval. On April 30 one infant was born, but the twin did not appear until September 13!

It is possible for pregnant women to lose one twin in a miscarriage but still carry the second child to full term without any damage resulting to it. This has happened rather frequently. Whether all these twins born far apart were identicals or fraternals is not known.

However, these twins are all "ordinary" in the sense that they were carried in one womb.

Superfetation and Superfecundation

Sometimes nature plays another trick. Occasionally mothers have two wombs and carry children simultaneously in both! Doctors argue about this. Some insist that these are not twins but merely superfetation in a woman who happened to have two wombs.

The successive fertilization in more than one intercourse of two or more eggs, formed at the *same* menstrual period, is called super-*fecundation*—that is, more than one impregnation.

But super*fetation,* meaning merely superpregnancy, is the supposed fertilization of two or more eggs released in *different* menstrual periods within a short interval. Geneticists dispute its actual occurrence in human beings, although it may explain the long intervals between some twin births.

Either process would explain the rare cases of "twins" having two fathers. And even with one father, should either pair really be called twins in the first place? Doctors may rightly argue, but we imagine some prejudiced mothers will flatly claim twins.

To the obstetrician a double-womb pregnancy is most unusual, though the mother hardly knows the difference. Perhaps only one woman in 160,000 has a double womb, and even in these rare cases it is extraordinary for a pregnancy to take place in both at once. Yet in 1953 two women, one in Brooklyn, New York, and one in Seekonk, Massachusetts, achieved the feat almost on the same day.

The Brooklyn mother, Mrs. Eugene Kupferstein, knew that she had two wombs, for her doctor had discovered this two years before when she had minor surgery to enable her to conceive. However, he had expected the coming twins to be from only one womb. When the second boy surprised him by being unready, he induced labor, and the brother was born. The Massachusetts woman, Mrs. Henry Peterson, apparently gave birth to both at once. However, these cases were not also delayed births, for both twins arrived on the same day.

Late in 1968 another double-womb case, with a fifty-day delay, made world headlines. The twenty-six-year-old mother, Maj-Britt Pettersson, of Motala, Sweden, already had two boys and was alarmed at having to rush to the hospital on November 1, three months ahead of time, for her third pregnancy. There the midwife (who in Sweden commonly relieves the doctor shortage) reassured her. After about ten minutes a little girl weighing barely above two pounds was put right into the incubator. Then the midwife's eyes popped. Her patient was still pregnant!

When the obstetrician arrived hastily, he determined to delay the birth if possible, because the first infant was so tiny. The most he hoped for was a few days, and he gave her an injection to block her body from releasing oxytocin, the hormone that activates uterine contractions. To his amazement days became weeks while she remained at the hospital. It became the talk of the town and later of the world when newspapers spread the story. Finally on the fiftieth day labor began for the second time, and little Elizabeth's brother, Klas, was born, still about a month premature but healthy.

In an article entitled "Twice a Mother in Thirty Days" Elizabeth Keiffer tells the story of the Pugh twins born in Pomona, California.[9] Here the double womb was not suspected until pregnancy was well advanced.

Betsy Pugh was delighted at the thought of twins, but it soon became apparent that instead of bulging normally in front, there were two pronounced bulges—one on each side. She experienced a great deal of morning sickness, lost weight, and could hardly sleep from one baby's kicking (the boy's!). She also had premature labor, but the doctor was able to prevent miscarriage.

Ten weeks later she was back in the hospital. The membranes had ruptured in one womb, and the baby would have to be delivered. Fifteen hours of labor ensued. Uneasily the doctor accelerated it with an injection, and little Lisa was safely born on February 18, 1966, weighing five pounds fourteen ounces.

But Betsy's ordeal had only begun. It might be a month more before the second baby came, the doctor told her! She went home in dismay. "Every time I'd cheer myself up thinking, 'Well, I have my little girl!' this kicking would start up near my ribs. Eric going *boom, boom, boom!*" She laughed. "I can joke about it now, but it sure didn't seem funny then!"

And Eric always seemed to kick the hardest when she was nursing Lisa, almost as if boy-girl jealousy can begin in the womb itself. The Pugh's firstborn, Glenn, was puzzled, too. Betsy had told him other mommies have just one baby, but she was such a very good mommy she was going to have two.

"Where is it?" he wanted to know. "Oh—still inside?"

But Betsy's worst embarrassment came when she took Lisa out in the carriage. "You can imagine how I felt wheeling my brand-new baby down the block—while I was nearly nine months pregnant with her brother! It was like being in a sideshow. I began bawling right in the street."

When Eric finally decided his time inside was up, a new complication arose. The womb that had held Lisa now obstructed the birth canal to prevent natural birth. So on March 19 Eric was delivered by cesarean section but without further trouble. He weighed a husky eight pounds two ounces.

The Pughs decided that when the twins are older, they will celebrate their birthdays on the actual dates. That way they'll really stay special. At least they were born in the same year!

Controlling the Genes

Scientists talk about "human engineering" as a prospect for the immediate future. Perhaps, they suggest, the blood supply to the fetus could be vastly improved for maximal brain growth and physical health. Perhaps stockpiles of synthetic proteins, antigens, enzymes, and hormones might be available.

Dr. Jean Rostand, in fact, predicts that "it will be little more than a game to change the subject's sex, the color of its eyes, the general proportions of body, limbs and perhaps the facial features."[10]

And certainly the number of infants a woman wished to bear at one time would be under control. Perhaps scientists could even transform the human female's placenta into one like that of Dr. Benirschke's admirable little armadillos—and reduce the risk of miscarriages, stillbirths, and abnormalities.

These problems of "algeny," or genetic alchemy, are vast, but the ethical problems stagger the mind. Who or what would be in control? Would it be altruistic or racial and political? Even if the former, would the altruist have a reasonable mind or be an "intellectual fool"?

Implantation . . . Prenatal Adoption

The artificial implantation of sperm is commonplace. If the difficult task of fertilizing the ova outside the body succeeds, they might someday be inserted by incision into the uterus.

Still another type of implantation has been suggested—"prenatal adoption," where an infertile woman wanting a child takes a fertilized cell from another woman to bear to full term. It is assumed that the actual pregnancy and birth will make for a closer relationship in the home. It might thus be possible to implant twins and bear infants related *to each other* but not to the legal parents.

Outside of adoption, people normally have only two parents, but with laboratory mice it can be different. On New Year's Day, 1965, the first "mosaic" mouse with *four parents* was born at the Institute for Cancer Research in Philadelphia. Five years later, Dr. Beatrice Mintz said, "We've raised over a thousand of these to ripe old age." She is now planning to try for six parents.[11]

The method is related to twinning, for two fertilized mouse eggs with a normal set of parents are permitted to divide a few times, then removed from their mothers into a culture medium for further growth. A chemical dissolves the membrane around each embryo, and the pair is pushed together so that the cell surfaces adhere. Thus a double-sized embryo is formed, which is then surgically inserted into the womb of a "pseudo-pregnant" mouse—one mated to a sterile male.

Cloning

Much more extraordinary among scientific experiments than mice with four parents is "cloning."

In a vial of tissue culture a single human cell can multiply to a million in a month's growth. Such a colony, all from one cell, is called a clone, and all the cells are identical except for rare cases of mutation. Thus each cell contains all the genetic information of the whole, and for experimental purposes is the equivalent of an intact whole.

So far it has been successful with frogs and more than fifty plants. The experiment results in exact duplicates in every detail, more identical than any "mere" identical twin. Clones might thus be termed "new age multiples," and the long-range picture is somewhat devastating.[12] Imagine a hundred Beethovens and a hundred Hitlers in the same world! The more far-out among scientists say this can actually happen.

In the experiment with frogs Dr. J. B. Gurdon, of Oxford University, England, took cells *not* from the sex glands, but from the intestines of *either* a male or a female frog. Removing the cell's nucleus, he implanted it in an unfertilized frog egg after destroying its own nucleus by radiation. More than 30 percent developed to the polliwog stage, and 1 to 2 percent matured into full-grown, fertile frogs.

No wonder the suggestion is made that dictators could take over the world and breed only extremes—a few leaders and supermen, carefully gradated, and millions of slaves!

All these bizarre speculations make *real* twins—the kind we've grown used to over the centuries without the intervention of human meddling—seem somehow cozier and more appealing.

The word "twin" itself is derived from an Anglo-Saxon source meaning "two strands twisted together." Even today the tangle is not always untied, and the union between the two can be close, mysterious, and at times unfathomable.

4 TWINS WHO FIND EACH OTHER

The romance of twins who are torn apart at birth, then united again after many years, is hoary with age. In thatched cottages around the peat fires or in the bleak halls of castles, those marvelous strangers—the tellers of tales, the troubadours, and the ballad singers—were always sure of a welcome. But the crispest chunk from the roast or the richest gift from the seigneur was theirs if they climaxed their repertoire with a story about twins who found each other!

Shakespeare, himself the father of twins, used the plot in several of his plays. Though weak in genetics with his "identical" boy-girl pairs, his audiences loved it. Even in our unromantic era the heart-tug never fails. Is it possible, we wonder, that not even great differences in upbringing can make these two products of the same minute embryonic speck into total unlikes?

In her text *The Science of Genetics* Professor Charlotte Auerbach writes:

> A rabid geneticist may wish for a chance of separating identical quadruplets at birth and having them reared in a Fifth Avenue apartment, an Indian wigwam, a Moscow orphanage and an Eskimo igloo, respectively; our society, fortunately, will not allow him to carry out such an experiment!

But if such a thing could be done, and forty years later these identical quads found each other, how alike would they be? Nobody can answer that question infallibly.

When Professor Newman did his pioneer work in the 1930's with identical twins separated at birth, he was able to find only twenty pairs for his studies. With his colleagues at the University of Chicago he had sent his "Calling All Twins" broadcasts out over the radio repeatedly. His favorite, though unproductive, reply was this: "My sister Pearl and I are twins. We do a specialty act at Minsky's. What's your proposition?"

Separated for Twenty-seven Years

Through radio and newspaper appeals the researchers offered trips to Chicago's Century of Progress for the ten best pairs in exchange for two days of their time.

One set, Gladys and Helen, had been separated at the age of eighteen months. Although each knew she was a twin, neither had ever tried to find the other. They did not meet until they were twenty-eight. Apparently by coincidence they settled in the same large Michigan city.

They found each other by another coincidence when one of Helen's school pupils asked why she had snubbed her the night before at a concert. Helen had not attended, but remembering her unknown twin, she asked several musicians if they had met her double. One of them directed her to a printer's shop, where the girls met at last.

Events in their lives had been very different. Helen, who had had two sets of foster parents, received a college education. Gladys, adopted by a Canadian railroad conductor in a remote part of the Rockies, never passed third grade. After holding various unskilled jobs, at twenty-one she married a mechanic and had two children. She endured many hardships with no softening graces.

Helen had not married until a year before their reunion, and her husband was prosperous. The twins were thirty-five when Newman interviewed them. Although still very alike in looks and mannerisms, Helen was well ahead on the basis of her IQ, but Gladys's 92 was high, considering her scanty education. Helen's handwriting was much more mature; both, however, made the letter "f" in the same peculiar way.

At the interview Gladys was shy, and Helen took the lead. Helen found new friends "tremendously exciting," whereas Gladys always feared people were talking about her. Discussing their marked divergence in ability and personality, Newman felt that this was caused by the great advantages enjoyed by Helen and the stress and deprivation Gladys had endured.

Influences of Heredity and Environment

Not all of Newman's twins liked each other on meeting. Two boys to whom the orphanage for some reason had given the same name— Paul Harold—lived with foster parents for twenty-three years not knowing of each other's existence. Paul Harold C. was a business-college graduate with a good position in a Grand Rapids furniture company. One day, rummaging through his parents' attic, he found some old letters and his birth certificate, which listed him as a twin.

He finally prevailed upon the orphanage to give him an address, and he traced his brother from place to place, winding up in a little rural community in Illinois. But when the brothers met on the Fourth of July, he was disappointed. His twin seemed so bucolic with his hearty, affable greeting that Paul C. found him uncouth. They couldn't find any bonds of understanding or warmth. Probably this was Paul C.'s own fault, for the professor's tests found him taciturn and dignified, with none of the comfortable small-town friendliness of his brother. Their personality tests were mixed, with confusing likenesses and differences. Newman wrote about them as follows:

> It appears there are two levels of behavior or expression of personality. One level that seems to be largely hereditary and is not modified much by differences in experience, and another level that is not hereditary and rather readily modified by the environment. The two Pauls were very similar in the first level of personality traits and quite different in the second, which included their mannerisms and attitudes toward each other and toward people in general.

This country-city, wealth-poverty distinction was fairly common. Newman wrote that it was hard to question the conclusion that within limits mental ability could be improved by education or suffer from the lack of it. The whole heredity-environment argument was not one problem but many, with no general solution. Much remained to be learned, he said.

His most interesting case, although familiar to many people, is too remarkable not to summarize. Twenty-two-year-old Edwin Iske was a repairman for the Bell Telephone Company when a new man arrived at work.

"Hello, Fred! How's tricks?" the stranger asked immediately.

Mildly surprised, Ed glanced closely at the newcomer. "You have me wrong. My name's not Fred."

"No?" The newcomer was suspicious. "What's the idea? Don't you know your old friend from Omaha?"

"Never saw you before in my life," Ed assured him.

The man still seemed skeptical, but Ed forgot it until another man hailed him as Fred and reacted just as dubiously. "Well, if you're not Fred, you're his dead ringer. I used to work with him in Omaha. He's a lineman, too."

This struck Ed as too big a coincidence. He visited his parents and questioned them about the matter. They finally confessed that he was adopted and told him that his real mother had died in giving birth to him and his identical twin.

Ed went to Omaha and was flabbergasted by a long series of astonishing coincidences. He and Fred Nestor had both been adopted by childless couples and had even attended the same big school briefly until Ed's family moved. Now they were both repairmen for the telephone company, after a similar education in similar homes; they had married girls of the same type in the same year, and both had four-year-old sons. But the real twist perhaps was that both had fox terriers named Trixie!

"I always felt that part of me was missing," said Ed. "Now I know why."

A Strange Tale of Parallels

Surely about the most startling experience one could have would be for a total stranger to appear and claim to be one's twin! One day in 1945 Marion Smith, a twenty-two-year-old clerk in a Toronto, Canada, department store, saw a customer looking across the counter at her with tears in her eyes. The other girl looked amazingly like herself, even to her very similar brown suit.

"I—I wonder if we could be twins?" the customer was asking timidly, putting out her hand.

The old story of surprise, disbelief, and wonder was replayed. To the other girl, Margaret Judson, the bewildered sense of something missing and the search of several years was at an end. She at least had known that she had either a twin or a double, but the idea was strange to Marion Smith.

To avoid arousing the floorwalker's ire, the two girls hastily arranged to meet the next day. For the following twenty-four hours Margaret was in a fever of suspense. She knew that she had been adopted at birth in Toronto. Then her foster family had moved across Canada to Vancouver. After joining the Canadian Women's Land Army in World War II, she was shipped east. Here she repeatedly met people who called her Marion and described an exact double. After the war she found work in the Toronto Post Office.

Next day both were again dressed alike in very similar plaid skirts, wearing little heart-shaped lockets, which had been the gifts of their foster mothers on their twenty-first birthdays!

Talking a mile a minute, they filled each other in on the past. The second girl, Marion Smith, had also tried to join the army but failed. Both girls were married to sailors of the same age, weight, and build who had been in the service four years and planned to make the navy their career.

Other strange parallels existed. In their teens both girls had been expert roller skaters and contemplated becoming professionals. Both had taken piano lessons during the same years, had sung alto in church choirs, and had had their tonsils removed during the same year.

From then on they kept in touch and eventually settled close-by each other in the state of Washington.[1]

This same surprise came to a young man named George Bueher, then of Flat Rock, Michigan. George, who was twenty-three at the time, was having dinner in Toledo, Ohio, when he looked up to see *himself* walking toward him across the restaurant floor.

"I wonder if you're my twin brother?" his mirror-image inquired.

George shook his head and flatly denied it, but the resemblance was so startling that he invited his alter ego to sit down. As he listened, amazement grew to wonder and wonder to a complete change of attitude. He "knew" he hadn't been adopted, and yet . . .

His table-mate introduced himself as William Esterline. He said that his parents had died when he was only three, and that he, his sister, and a twin brother were placed in a children's home in Miami,

Florida. Later they were adopted into separate foster homes. Mr. and Mrs. Esterline had told William the whole story when he was small, and for some twenty years he had been on the lookout for his twin.

After a long discussion, George invited William to go home with him to Flat Rock. When she saw the amazing likeness, Mrs. Bueher realized her twenty-year-old secret had been exposed. She had wanted George to grow up as her own beloved son and so had kept the fact of adoption from him. Now she confessed that William Esterline had to be his twin brother, for she had found George in a children's home in Miami![2]

The case of Tony Milasi and Roger Brooks has been told many times, yet some of the amazing coincidences bear repeating. Reared in foster homes over a thousand miles apart, both boys knew that they had been twins separated immediately after birth. When Roger entered the air force, another soldier described seeing his double playing basketball in a Catholic school in Binghamton, New York.

But in response to his written inquiry, the school only sent him a rosary. Roger, raised in a Jewish home, was understandably peeved. Even as a child he had dreamed of his twin. Further attempts to find his brother failed.

Meanwhile, Tony had similar experiences. The doctor and his parents thought his twin had died, but he had been stopped in the navy by GIs who thought they knew him. When he got out of the service, he managed a crew of book salesmen.

One boy, Mark, stayed with Tony only briefly, since he was returning to Miami, Florida, when the university opened again in the fall. It was there, in Miami, that Mark, working as busboy in a restaurant, ran into Roger, and following the old familiar pattern, called him Tony.

When he learned that Roger actually had a lost twin, Mark was very excited. He was sure he knew him! But Roger had been disappointed too often. He met Mark next day and got him to call the book company and ask the date of Tony's birth.

"Tony Milasi was born May 28, 1938," Mark announced, coming out of the phone booth. "In Binghamton, New York."

"So was I!" Roger exclaimed. From then on things began to open up. Social workers, now intrigued, helped, and the brothers talked by telephone.

When they finally met, they were fascinated not only by their great likeness but by trivialities. They smoked the same brand of cigarettes and used the same after-shave lotion and even the same toothpaste— a little-known brand made in Denmark. Their dental problems were alike; they even had similar scars on their arms. These curious small coincidences constantly crop up to baffle investigators engaged in twin research.[3]

The Medical Examiner's Office in New York City, in addition to its daily investigation of murder, is sometimes asked to work in non-criminal cases. Back in 1947 Dr. Alexander S. Wiener headed the department of serology and bacteriology, established less than a decade before. Under Wiener's direction the department had won international fame for the discovery of subclassifications of blood types running into the thousands.

Thus it was not an unusual occurrence when a transatlantic flight from Switzerland brought vials of blood containing samples from three small boys and three parents. Two of the boys were certainly twins—but were they the same two who six years before had been breast-fed by an adoring mother?[4]

On July 4, 1941, Mme. Madeleine Joye gave birth to twins at the Misericordia Clinic, Fribourg, Switzerland. World War II was raging, and the little Alpine country, in deadly fear of invasion by the Nazis, was mobilizing. In all Swiss hospitals the medical staffs had been cut to the bone, and at Misericordia nurses were working fifty to sixty hours without sleep.

The Joyes brought home beautiful twin boys. Certainly they were nonidentical, for Paul was husky, and Philippe, named for his father, was slight and sensitive. But both were equally beloved. One day the senior Philippe Joye attended a party at the home of M. and Mme. Vatter, the most influential family in the town. When a little boy entered and was introduced as their son Ernst, Joye was dumb-founded. Ernst was the image of his own son and namesake, Philippe! He could hardly take his eyes off the boy—voice, mannerisms, features, were so fantastically similar.

Then came the day when all three boys enrolled at the convent school, and a nun seated young Philippe Joye and Ernst Vatter side by side on the bench together, thinking they were twins. All the sisters and the children laughed at the mistake, but it continued to be re-

peated there and on the streets of the rather small city. The Joyes
were intrigued and amused—until the school's annual June fête.

This was the first time they themselves saw Philippe and Ernst
together in identical costumes. Astonished, they went to see Mme.
Vatter, who had since become a widow. Had her son Ernst by any
chance been born at the clinic on the same day as the Joye twins?
When the answer was *yes,* they were badly troubled, and more so
when, through the dentist, they learned that both Philippe and Ernst
had only two lower incisors.

Their doctor, who had ridiculed the idea of a hospital mix-up, now
suggested checking records at the clinic. One placenta would suggest
that the doubles, Ernst and Philippe, were really twins. When this
was confirmed, the Joyes went to Mme. Vatter again. She simply did
not care. Having just lost her husband, was she also to be asked to
surrender her darling Ernst—to strangers?

But the doctor was now insisting on proper tests, and there was the
legal angle. Mme. Vatter was wealthy, and if Philippe were truly her
son, he would be cheated out of his inheritance. Blood typing by the
usual tests of that era proved nothing. All seven of them, including
Mme. Vatter's ten-year-old daughter, were type A.

Eight months' research finally established that Philippe and Ernst
must have emerged from the same womb. As final proof, the vials of
blood were sent to Dr. Wiener in New York to check the sub-
groupings.

The blood of Paul Joye, the supposed twin, was typed A_1MNrh.
Philippe and Ernst were $A_1MNRh_1Rh_2$. Mme. Vatter was A_1MN-Rh_1rh. Like Paul, she had the small rh factor in her blood, and Mme.
Joye did not. Dr. Wiener said this proved that Mme. Vatter was the
true mother of Paul "Joye" and that Mme. Joye actually had given
birth to identical, not fraternal, twins—who thus had to be Philippe
and Ernst!

Mme. Vatter still wanted the final test—skin-grafting among the
three boys. When those between Philippe and Ernst "took" while
Paul's withered away, debate was no longer possible. At the births the
exhausted staff at the war-beleaguered hospital had somehow mixed
up the babies.

But the boys were now seven years old, devoted to their supposed
families. For extroverted Paul the shock was cushioned by the fact
that he would be rich and ride to school in an automobile. He made

the change excitedly, sure that his fairy godmother was in charge. But young Ernst was hostile and aloof. For months he called his new mother "madame" and resisted all caresses. The only thing that helped was that he now had a father. Otherwise, he said frankly, he would leave!

Eventually Ernst was won over. Three years later when the boys were questioned, he said of his new twin, "It's wonderful! Now I have my other half."

Young Paul Vatter was frank to the point of bluntness. "I like it here much better. We have a bigger car!"

It was really Mme. Vatter who was the loser. Unlike Mme. Joye, she did not get a mirror-likeness of a child she already had, but a stranger. True, he looked like her husband, but he was not the baby she had nursed.

Both mothers grieved for the children they had lost. Perhaps only the doctors and the law were wholly satisfied.

Together and Apart

About a quarter of a century after Newman's research a British psychiatrist at Maudsley Hospital in London, James Shields, dug still deeper into the question of heredity versus environment.[5]

As we have learned, fraternal twins can differ as greatly as any other brothers and sisters, since they are the products of different ova and different sperm which just happen to develop simultaneously in the same womb. But there *is* one way in which fraternals are like identicals, yet different from the other siblings—their environment.

They are born together into the same psychological, emotional, and financial situation. They can't be an only child, and they share whatever environment—happy or unhappy, comfortable or impoverished—happens to exist in that family at that time.

The next child may arrive when the parents are wealthier, happier, more competent as parents—or instead, when they are ill, unemployed, or wanting a divorce. So in this one respect fraternals and identicals are alike—although the fraternals, with quite different personalities, will, of course, react to that family situation quite differently, whereas the identicals are more apt to share the same reaction.

Thus when Dr. Shields succeeded in finding forty-four pairs of

identical twins separated at birth—an extraordinary feat in itself—
and a control group of forty-four identicals reared together plus thirty-
two pairs of same-sex frats, he had what every research worker
dreams of finding—a near-perfect setup for establishing the importance of heredity and environment.

Most of the twins were found through a B.B.C. television program
entitled "Twin Sister, Twin Brother," televised in London in November, 1953. Simultaneously the *Radio Times* printed a questionnaire
for all twins to send in. Some five thousand twins did so, and the
program passed on to Shields those from all twin pairs of the same
sex who had been reared apart. From a careful follow-up of these
cases and the control group he began his enormous task.

Dr. Shields's book is full of complex charts and tables, and his
conclusions at times seem equally complex, for twins are still individuals. Although he never states flatly that heredity is more important than environment, he does say that the genes are a blueprint. In
personality, mannerisms, life attitudes, and IQs, identical twins who
had seldom or never met until maturity amazed even their mates by
great similarities. All of his separated pairs had been brought up in
different homes for at least five years, usually having been parted in
infancy. He tested most pairs himself, frequently in their own homes.
The youngest were eight and a half, the oldest fifty-nine. The ages of
the controls matched closely. Some never knew they had a twin until
the investigation began.

Like Newman, Shields found that although the twin who broke
away from his birth environment paid a higher price in greater tensions and difficulty in making friends, he was usually more sophisti-
cated and successful as a result of the stress. But the twin whom he
would have expected to be the more neurotic often wasn't. One,
reared by three spinster aunts and a bachelor uncle and made to be
grandma's pet, was actually the stronger character and happier in her
marriage—proud of her gift for looking after her older relatives.

Twins having the least contact often proved more alike than those
who lived together. Probably thirty-five out of his forty-four sets had
a leader—usually the more extroverted one. Thus twins reared
together will differ more in their extroversion than if separated,
because separated twins will have escaped the feeling of competition.
If the home is disturbed, identicals will be less close.

Jessie and Winifred, eight-and-a-half-year-old twins, the illegitimate daughters of an American GI and a London girl, were separated at three months and adopted. Although they grew up almost in the same block, there was no contact between the families. Repeatedly the children were greatly attracted in school, but Jessie's mother kept separating them and got her a permanent wave so they wouldn't look so much alike.

Both were bright, talkative, inquisitive children, and the very different attitudes of the foster mothers had made almost no difference. Their teacher said when they first met at school, not knowing they were twins, "They were never apart, wanted to sit at the same desk, and progressed at the same rate."

Dr. Shields was able to follow up these twins when they were sixteen. They were still much alike, with Jessie perhaps better adjusted at home. She was working in a bank, and Winifred was preparing to teach physical education.

Twins Madeleine and Lillian met through his program at the age of thirty-six. When she was twenty-one, Madeleine was told she was adopted, and later learned she had been a twin, so she wrote to the television program to ask if her sister could be traced. The orphanage complied, and after the interview the sisters frequently wrote to each other. Even as children both had longed for a sister. Madeleine had pretended her pillow was her sister, as Lillian had with her teddy bear.

Both giggled, had loud voices, and were very emotional. The similarities in their lives had been most striking. Both sang in church choirs, did door-to-door selling, and performed comedy roles in amateur theatricals. Both loved animals and had uncommon pets.

Habits such as rubbing their noses, rocking if tired, and becoming easily flustered were shared. When Dr. Shields saw them again at age forty-two, differences were difficult to find. Madeleine, who had bought a fish-and-chips shop after losing her husband, found her sister and the family closeness a great comfort.

Among all of Shields's cases, Herta and Berta had the most unusual lives. They were born in South America, separated at four, and did not actually meet again until middle age.

Their father, a Scandinavian ship's carpenter who ran a home for seamen, was a hot-tempered, boastful, unreliable man, always embroiled in elaborate schemes for salvaging sunken treasure. When his debts reached many thousands of pounds, he settled them by selling the children! But four-year-old Herta wouldn't accept this fate. She screamed and refused food so steadily that the French family who had purchased her brought her back in two weeks.

Little Berta was more docile. She was sold to a doctor and his wife, of Scandinavian descent but Spanish-speaking, and was brought up in the Latin American city where she still lives. She was very fond of her kindly foster father and obedient to his difficult, often cantankerous wife. From recurrent dreams and the servants' remarks she sensed that she was adopted. When she was eleven, her foster mother admitted it, but told her that her father ("a drunkard") and her mother ("a bad woman") were now dead.

After Herta was returned to her real parents, the child lived in lonely places in South America with no schooling. Her father grew more and more violent. When she was nine, her mother took her back to her own former home in a rural Scandinavian community. Repeatedly they tried to write to Berta but were told she had "disappeared." Later letters were always returned unopened. When the father joined them, he became manic-depressive.

Thus in contrast to her more fortunate twin, Herta had an extremely hard childhood. At twelve she began delivering laundry and eventually owned her own restaurant and entertained as a singer with her guitar. Her first husband proved to be a drunken sadist who tried to strangle her. She had no security until, at thirty-five, she married an English sergeant in the Royal Air Force and accompanied him back to England.

About this time Berta intercepted a letter from her father to her foster parents. Soon the twins were happily, but secretly, writing and exchanging gifts. Berta had had a good education and was genuinely devoted to her doctor "father" and his wife, in spite of the latter's fierce determination to keep the girls apart by means of lies. Berta also had married at twenty-two, but much more securely. Her French husband, twelve years older, was the owner of a nearby factory. They owned a town house and a villa. Like Herta, she had no children.

Reunited by letters, the twins happily exchanged measurements, lingerie, and cosmetics, although they still had to play a complicated game of make-believe, because Berta's aging foster mother wouldn't admit that Herta existed.

"We are so alike!" Berta wrote. "Sentimental, romantic, dreaming all the time."

They developed an intense affection for each other. Letters supplied the warmth they had missed. Even their childhood nicknames were alike. Berta was called Pussy because she purred when pleased, and Herta became Pussa, "cuddly like a cat." Gay, changeable, and lively, they both had high moral standards. Herta had surmounted a very difficult childhood with strong courage.

Both had a deformity of the opposite foot, had skin rashes, and walked in their sleep. Although Berta had had much the easier life, she pampered herself and was always taking pills. Herta had undergone some psychiatric sessions for severe depressions but had much more vitality and drive. Their case, Dr. Shields wrote, was "remarkable for human interest, extremes of geographical and cultural separation and the very great temperamental similarity."

At forty-nine, on Berta's first visit to Europe, the twins met at last. For both it was a joyous experience. Each said the other was exactly as she expected.

5 PSYCHOLOGEMINI

It is not our intention to present quantities of alarming statistics that would frighten expectant mothers. Twins have been arriving since the days of the caveman and no doubt will continue with about the same frequency. If multiples are suspected in your womb, the best possible advice is not to work yourself into a tizzy. It has happened before, and other mothers who have "been there" are probably even more comforting than medical consultations. Our chapter on the twin clubs (Chapter 14) will lead you to them. Their members will tell you that once the first months of confusion are conquered, twins can be fun.

But there are certain facts about twinship that are helpful to know. Some are present in all pregnancies but emphasized in multiple births; others are the result of this extra strain on the mother.

For singletons their order of birth into a family plays its part in developing or repressing egos and personalities. But with normal, healthy twins it is ridiculous to create imagined superiority by family chatter as to which twin "came first." Sometimes, however, the difference is obvious, for the firstborn twin is the luckier. If either is handicapped, it is more apt to be the second, who may have been more cramped or undernourished in the womb.

Even when twins are not called premature, they usually average only 259 days in the womb compared to the singleton's 280. A mild degree of prematurity seems to safeguard twins against toxemia and birth complications, and they actually have a better chance of survival than some single "preemies," for the cause is not so apt to be something amiss in the mother. Their smaller size is natural, too, and less cause for alarm.

But the physical handicaps of great prematurity are obvious, and such babies are now found to be more prone to emotional problems later if isolation in hospital nurseries has deprived them of cuddling and affection.

Dr. Marshall Klaus, of Babies Hospital in Cleveland, watched movies that compared mothers holding their full-term babies right after delivery with those who had to wait weeks to cuddle their preemies. He said these deprived mothers seemed unable to react normally. "They looked as if they were picking flies off their babies!" he commented.

Many people do not realize that childbirth is painful to the child, too. And especially so when more than one infant is cramped inside the womb. Consider what the baby goes through when brutally forced out of his safe warm world where he has floated in his own private pond. No wonder these sudden contractions make him arrive with a scream, exhausted, sometimes injured, and dazed by the brilliant light!

Professor O. S. Heyns, former head of the Department of Obstetrics and Gynecology at the University of Witwatersrand, South Africa, has for many years used a "birth suit" to ease and speed delivery for mothers and babies. It is simply an abdominal decompression chamber which relaxes the womb. For the last ten weeks of pregnancy the mother either attends a clinic or rents a suit for daily treatment at home.

Made of airtight plastic supported by a light framework, it covers her from feet to chest, leaving the arms free. She controls the pressure herself and is perfectly comfortable while the suit reduces muscle tension that cramps the uterus. Birth later is rapid and easy.

"It was bliss!" said one mother whose labor with her firstborn had lasted thirty-six hours.

Doctors claim that fetal distress is cut by 80 percent. It is well known that the emerging infant's brain sometimes receives too little oxygen—affecting intelligence. Use of the suit prevents this deprivation.

Dr. Heyns claims that his more than ten thousand "decompression babies," including many twins, develop faster and are more robust. None has had cerebral palsy, which averages once in one thousand births. Their language skills are exceptional, many talking well at a year and a half.[1]

Thirty or more United States and Canadian doctors are also experimenting, amid great argument, with a similar "baby bubble." Nurses say they can tell which mothers have used a decompression device by "which ones are yelling and which ones smiling. And the babies come out pink and sassy." But doctors, who (unless female) never feel birth pains themselves, are well known to be slow to accept such innovations.

Other obstetricians believe that with twins the cord should not be cut too quickly. Their survival can depend on their being allowed to receive all the blood from the placenta. As much as an extra third of a pint may pour into the baby if it is held a few inches below the uterus until the pulsations of the cord cease.

Many famous men have begun life several weeks ahead of time, yet premature infants, twins or single-born, do average about twice the rate of deficiencies. If children are born less than a year after a previous birth, they then have lower weights and IQs and more neurological problems. A recent government study states, "The mother perhaps has had insufficient time to restore supplies of critical nutrients required by the fetus for normal development of the brain." In earlier centuries when all mothers nursed their babies for several years, the interval between births averaged about two and a half years.

Many factors escape notice in coldly impersonal statistics. It is the percentage of handicapped twins in such statistics that probably creates a prevalent opinion that twins are not quite as smart as singletons.

The IQs of identicals are usually about 3.5 points closer than those of fraternals, which, in turn, are closer than those of other siblings in the family.

A lack of stimulating experiences in a busy home also has a dulling effect on infants. In a Harvard University experiment with orphaned babies Doctors Burton White and Jerome Kagan have shown that dramatic differences in infant mental and personality development are attained through training in the crib. "The baby is a novelty-digesting machine that devours change. Pushing him to new experiences keeps him moving," says Kagan.[2]

By contrast to this lively environment, orphans found in an institution in the Near East could not even sit up at two years or walk at four, because they were left alone so much.

Chemical Imbalance and Retardation

Research today tends more and more to suggest that chemical imbalance is one cause of retardation and that vitamins and medication can be of radical help in preventing and improving such conditions in the future.

One of the pioneers in this belief was Dr. Franz Kallmann, who at the time of his early work was head of the Medical Genetics Department at New York State Psychiatric Institute. Before he died he had studied more than seven thousand twins. Convinced that someday chemical treatment would provide the answer, Kallmann rejected the prevalent notion that bad circumstances were the cause of mental trouble. If so, why did others in the family escape? Those who succumbed had a special genetic weakness, he said. Harsh circumstances were only the trigger.

With his studies of disturbed identicals he found that 86.2 percent shared the affliction of schizophrenia; and with manic-depressive twins, 95.7 percent were both victims. If the genes develop a defense against such breakdowns, then surely the process "can be identified and somehow duplicated biochemically."

Later doctors found that the hormones manufactured by the adrenal glands are not quite the same—chemically or in quantity—in schizophrenics as in normal people. Since the adrenals bolster the body against shock, this may mean less built-in protection from nervous breakdowns.

One of Dr. Kallmann's cases of elderly twins, Mrs. Mills and Miss Beach, had been separated at eighteen. Miss Beach spent forty-seven years in the Orient as a missionary and on retirement joined her widowed sister, who had been a farmer's wife. Yet, at sixty-five, when they met the doctor, the two women were almost identical in appearance and personality, with very similar IQs.[3]

Another of his pairs, Clara and Dora, however, illustrate the power of a protected environment. Given out for adoption separately as infants, Clara was lovingly cared for and married a well-to-do man, whereas Dora had a troubled childhood and a harsh marriage. Both were neurotic and had been dull in school. Clara was given to crying jags but was eased through them by a fond older husband. Dora succumbed to mental illness before the menopause and was committed to a mental institution.

But these distressing cases are not the rule. Many twins have outstanding minds with IQs near or above the genius level. In his excellent book *Twins and Supertwins* Amram Scheinfeld mentions National Merit Scholarship winners Philip and Elmer Schaefer, of Elmhurst, Illinois. Although premature fraternals, they rated among the highest ever recorded for high-school students. He also mentions an unusual two-generation twin family, all with exceptionally high IQs.[4] Identical triplets, Charles A., Robert B., and Richard C. Fenwick, were graduated from Purdue University with identical scholastic records—perfect six-point averages.

Negro twins have also scored high among these superior minds. *Ebony* magazine (September, 1965) mentions Nathan and Benjamin White. Benjamin is *Ebony*'s sales-promotion manager in New York, and Nathan, a Harvard Ph.D., heads the social-work program of the Episcopal Church Diocese of Newark, New Jersey.

In support of various doctors' convictions that both retardation and mental illness may often be the result of chemical imbalance in the brain is the recent work of the distinguished biochemist and Nobel Prize winner, Dr. Linus Pauling.

Offering impressive evidence, Dr. Pauling argues that if there is a gene through which schizophrenia is inherited, it may be one which does not affect the brain directly, but the chemical mix upon which the brain feeds. Deficiencies of vitamins C and B_{12}, glutamic, folic, and nicotinic acids, thiamin, and other chemical substances have been noted in schizophrenic patients.

Certain lower animals are able to produce some of their own vitamins, but man is dependent for his upon proper diet. Dr. Bernard Rimland, psychologist and director of the Institute for Child Study Research, San Diego, California, says, "Authorities are becoming more convinced that mentally ill children and adults actually have a metabolic or biochemical defect that disrupts their perception and thinking." Urine samples are being taken from these children both before and after vitamin dosages based upon body weights. "If the body uses up the vitamins for metabolism, they won't be excreted. Studies suggest that mentally ill children *need up to 1,000 times more vitamins* than normal children."

Although many psychiatrists, frozen in theories of sexual traumas, remain hostile to suggestions of physical remedies, physicians know of twenty to thirty forms of brain impairment caused by the inability of some newborn infants to handle certain chemicals in their food.

After six years' work with amino acids, Dr. Georges Ungar at Baylor Medical College in Houston, Texas, announced a discovery late in 1970. From the brains of rats conditioned to fear instead of love darkness, he has isolated a peptide chain of fifteen of the twenty amino acids. By feeding this substance to other rats, the fear is transferred.

This seems to prove that memory can be carried from one individual to another and is actually stored within a physical structure. He suggests that the learning mechanism depends on the increased formation of proteins in the brain. Learning may thus be impaired if such formation is halted. Strangely, the brain cells contain much more protein than other far more active body cells.

The Genain Quadruplets

We must not underestimate the part that faulty upbringing can play in mental breakdowns with twins and multiples. The most appalling case we encountered was the subject of a book, *The Genain Quadruplets,* by Dr. David Rosenthal.[5] It details the story of mentally disturbed parents who really did drive their four little girls into insanity.

"Genain" was a pseudonym chosen by the psychiatrist from the Greek words meaning "dire birth" or "dreadful gene." The girls, born within seventeen minutes of each other, were exploited from the first. Visitors were charged to see them, and they were constantly exhibited in public.

Their mother, who had almost a psychosis on the subject of masturbation, went berserk when she discovered this fairly common tendency in the girls. Somehow she was able to find an incredibly permissive and stupid doctor who supported her sadistic ideas to the point of sexual mutilation. Two of the children were subjected to clitoridectomies and all of them to incessant spying, so that the wonder is not their eventual breakdowns, but that any of them were able to function well enough to earn a living at all.

The girls had no friends. Starved for affection, they lived only as a unit, and at school they were disliked, envied, and isolated. In her huge scrapbooks of clippings Mrs. Genain created "a kind of looking glass in which the girls could gaze at their own reflections and learn something of who and what they were and were expected to be."

And they were expected to be far too much—in all the wrong areas. Kept as pitiful freaks in their mother's private zoo, the night-marish atmosphere almost makes one accept the Victorian concept of "bad seed." Surely the most normal of children, dropped into that sick environment for twenty-five years, would have succumbed.

Two of the girls fought valiantly for normality, and when, one by one, they were institutionalized, the doctors observed that "Myra" might not have been considered truly schizoid had she not been what the neighbors called "one of those queer quads." Of the four, she was released and she married—an immature man, but she was fairly content—and the second girl made a marginal adjustment outside the hospital. The sicker pair are still institutionalized, and the one who was most severely badgered is considered hopeless.

Obviously it is not just the fact of multiple birth that creates such problems, but multiples plus family. Action and reaction within the home, the capacity for sharing, love and its encouragement, are the determinants. This is true even for singletons—and how much more so for those infants who are prima donnas privately and publicly from their first wailing breaths!

Twins and Sexual Deviation

Congenital deviations in the sexual organs sometimes occur with multiple births. True hermaphrodites (who have both ova- and sperm-producing organs) are extremely rare, but twins have been found among them. In ancient times such births were used by fortune-tellers to predict the downfall of royalty, or they were put to death. Others became mountebanks who claimed to cure by touching.

Pseudo-hermaphrodites also occur—though rarely—among twins. The condition is not always recognized immediately, for the child has the internal organs of one sex but externally appears like the opposite sex. Their real sex may be manifested at adolescence, when the hormones appropriate to their internal organs begin to be produced. Sometimes an operation can help the condition.

Although the sex of the child is determined at the moment of conception, its future sex organs are simply cell masses that begin to rearrange into a structural forecast, then take on a pattern from which either sex can develop. If hormone production is delayed, haphazard development can produce organs that are not clear-cut as male or female.

Homosexuality is another area where identicals are usually alike, but among fraternals, less than half share the deviation.

The tendency to be attracted to one's own sex in greater or lesser degree is almost universal at some stage of growth, and it is claimed that everyone has the potential for being homosexual—that there is no such thing as a clear-cut, 100 percent heterosexual. But this latent tendency may never manifest itself in either action or conscious desire.

Psychiatrists and geneticists disagree as to whether environment or heredity plays the larger part here. But if a genetic trend exists, it is not apt to develop without emotional stresses in the home. When the father is too passive, an aggressive mother may sometimes unconsciously stimulate a sex response in her sons because of her own frustrations.

In two cases of homosexual twins the mothers were disappointed by having boy instead of girl babies. One of these women even bathed her boys into their late teens while wearing transparent or no clothing herself.

Of these two pairs of twins, one set remained together and became a homosexual couple; the other two sought separate partners. As with the sad little Genain quadruplets, these children would have developed more happily had the parents not been neurotic themselves.

With homosexuality there may also be a chemical cause, just as with retardation. Dr. Tommy Evans, of Wayne State University, says that tranquilizers, which some pregnant women "take by the bucketful," have caused irreversible damage to sexual development in baby rats born of tranquilized mothers. Dr. Evans believes that these drugs may explain some of the "aberrant sex behavior we see in humans—boys wanting to be girls and girls wanting to be boys." Mothers may be creating these sex behavior patterns for their own offspring chemically as well as emotionally by indiscriminate use of tranquilizers.[6]

But so far as we know, no twin has ever had one of the current, though also rare, sex-change operations. In England (under certain conditions and for their citizens only) transsexual operations may be performed free under the National Health Service.[7]

Twin Likeness in Crime

The likeness among identicals is also pronounced in crime. But here there is an even stronger likelihood of the home background being the impelling influence. However, the same concordance is too often found among twins who were reared apart to deny a hereditary tendency.

In the period between the two world wars various European researchers used twins in analyzing the causal factors involved in criminality and disagreed only on minor points. Professor Johannes Lange studied criminal twins—thirteen MZ (identical) and seventeen DZ (fraternal). He found that ten of the thirteen identicals were similar in criminal behavior, but with the seventeen fraternals, fifteen were involved in totally different crimes.[8]

Lange's sixth identical pair, Ferdinand and Luitpold Schweizer, were separated at the age of eight. Both had criminal records and similar personalities, but by the age of thirty-three there were considerable differences in social behavior. Lange described Luitpold as "a respectable workman, a fireside hero who weeps in church," whereas Ferdinand was restless, drunken, and "given to hawking in the company of low females." Both lacked will power and did better under strict discipline—"Ferdinand in the army, Luitpold when managed by an energetic, strong-minded wife."

In the United States Dr. A. A. Rosanoff reported in 1941 that out of 137 sets of identicals—with only 18 exceptions—where one was a delinquent or "disordered," so was the other. These twins were compared with 272 sets of fraternals, but as he included mixed-sex twins, his 170 cases with only one delinquent may not be conclusive.

Professor Charlotte Auerbach in her *Science of Genetics* stated that the concordance of delinquency among identicals is more than twice as high as with fraternals. Her twins frequently took to the same type of crime after many years of separation.

"Criminality, like mental disease," she wrote, "appears to be the result of unfavorable environmental circumstances acting on a genetically receptive constitution."

The Idiot-Savants

Probably the most bizarre and baffling twins in the world are George and Charles, the "idiot-savants." A "wise idiot" is a confusion of terms, but psychologists apply the classification to a feeble-minded individual of any grade who shows remarkable talent in some one direction. These talents are always self-acquired, for such individuals are not teachable. George and Charles, who so far as is known are the only twins to have this peculiarity, might be called "calendar" encyclopedias.

Dr. William Horwitz, the psychiatrist to whom they are warmly devoted, will ask them: "Can you tell me in what years April first falls on Sundays?"

Rocking back and forth in delight at their own helpfulness, the boys chant together, "1968, 1963, 1957, 1946," and if he doesn't stop them, they are overjoyed to carry the dates back for hundreds of years. Correctly! And if the date is within their life-span, they can add the weather, which nurse had a cold, or what patient left the hospital.

Yet they can't add six and three, nor make change. They can supply answers to "impossible" questions, said *The New York Times,* but not to easy ones! They are usually model patients, eager to do simple routine chores such as delivering linen and mail at the New York State Psychiatric Institute. Neatly dressed and cheerful, they seldom display any of the violence they showed in childhood.

They look about fifteen, but their IQs have risen at the institute from 30–40 to 60–70, demonstrating that intelligence can improve under special and kindly care. But their poor memory for all facts except dates makes teaching them nearly impossible.

George can play the "dating game" over an incredible range of seven thousand years; Charles knows the score for only about two thousand. There are no calendars going back seven thousand years! How do they do it?

"We do it, we do it!" they say proudly when asked. "It's in our heads."

The idiot-savant twins are not lightning calculators—those rare persons who can do fantastic sums in their heads. Their abilities lie only with dates and the trivial events associated with those dates.

Occasionally they still "go on a toot," as they put it, and have violent spells if someone forgets and does a chore that the boys had taken over as their own responsibility. But with a skill that normal persons might envy, they have learned then to soothe their own anger by bursting into a rousing rendition of "The Star-Spangled Banner" or by playing their Beethoven records.

The psychiatrists continue to ponder their skills and their handicaps. They think that the twins may have developed a special type of memory unlike normal intelligence processes.

"The feeling now in some circles," says Dr. Horwitz, "is that the memory function has a lot to do with the protein chemistry of the brain. I wonder if the protein chemistry of their brains is different from that of other people? Or the rest of their chemistry? [Here] there may be a key somewhere to memory function."[9]

6 TOGETHERNESS FROM WOMB TO TOMB

To everything there is a season, and a time to every purpose under the heaven: A time to be born, and a time to die; . . . A time to kill, and a time to heal; a time to break down, and a time to build up; A time to weep, and a time to laugh; . . . A time to get, and a time to lose; . . . A time to love, and a time to hate.

Ecclesiastes 3:1–8

Perhaps nowhere is this scriptural declaration of cycles in human life more emphasized than with twins. In these lives of Tweedledum and Tweedledee many events are twice-told tales. From diaper duos to duplicate deaths their days seem filled with puzzling parallels. Marriages, childbirth, accidents, honors, and even deaths often occur at the same time.

Twin sisters who give birth themselves on the same day are almost commonplace.

Some years ago in New York City Dr. Henry Aronson delivered twins: Katherine and Winifred Devine. Then on September 20, 1947, he again assisted when the twins had their own babies (nontwins). Another pair, Mrs. Dorothy McDonald and Mrs. Helen McDonald, became engaged to and then married brothers on the same days and gave birth to babies less than an hour apart.

Total Synchronization

In Salt Lake City one set of twin sisters became such models of "synchronicity" that they gave birth to their *fourth* child on the same

65

day of the same month and at the same hour as their other three children! And at Chilton Memorial Hospital, Pompton Plains, New Jersey, on July 31, 1962, twin sisters each had a set of twins on their own thirtieth birthday. Moreover, the two new sets of twins were born at the same hour as their mothers, about seven minutes apart.[1]

The same sort of thing is constantly happening with mishaps—broken or sprained limbs, automobile accidents in separate places, illnesses, surgical operations for the same emergency. An AP news photograph shows Mrs. Saveta Martin and her twin, Miss Sophia Deretich, both wearing neck braces as the result of *separate* auto accidents in Los Angeles. Girl twins in Lubbock, Texas, although in different cars several miles apart, slammed car doors almost simultaneously on their left hands.

In 1955 the *Journal of the American Medical Association* reported an odd case of identical twins—Cleveland, Ohio, housewives temporarily separated by some three thousand miles. Both were stricken with a very unusual disease—sarcoidosis, a chronic infection affecting the eyes and face—only a few months apart.

We also have quite a collection of freak coincidences with twins that are pure chance, without genetic reasons or subtle influences. Here is one from the hundreds of letters we have received since we began this research:

> My sister and I are identical twins born in Canton, Ohio. Our maiden name was Cunningham. She is now Joy Coldsnow, I am Joan Bryan.
>
> The first funny thing I remember was when we were about six. A family friend from St. Paul's Episcopal Church asked our parents if we could draw tickets at a parish party. People bought whole books of tickets (five in a book) and other parents bought just one apiece.
>
> During the drawing I drew out a ticket that belonged to my mother. She was ill at home that evening, so Dad went forward to get her prize. He didn't even get back to his seat before my sister pulled out the next ticket—and that belonged to him! This got a laugh we'll never forget!

The city fathers of Akron, Ohio, dreamed up a vacation-time gimmick by tagging seventy fish out of some fifteen thousand in the park pond. Children under fifteen who caught a tagged fish were given silver dollars. Their statistics state that one child catching a "silver-dollar fish" has 1 chance in 218, and two children, 1 in 5,600. But on their very first try at the fishing game, not only did Larry and Jerry Adaska, twelve-year-old twins, catch tagged fish almost simultaneously, but both fish were blue gills of the same weight!

No one can account for such freak coincidences, but mishaps and illnesses are sometimes induced by sympathy. If one twin is hurt or sick, the other may subconsciously duplicate the circumstance through the closeness of the tie.

Physical and Psychological Parallelism

Both physically and psychologically there can be remarkable parallelism between identicals. Since MZ twins were originally a single egg, it is not surprising if their behavior patterns, favorite colors, tastes, and preferences remain the same throughout their lives. The motivations for their acts may originate from both their genes and their shared environment—such as a case of twin nuns who took their final vows together.

The physical parallelism can be quite impressive. In Germany before World War II Professor Vogt studied nineteen pairs of identical twins.[2] His article about them in *Hamburger Illustrierte* said that in old age even their wrinkles repeated the same fine network, and any bodily impairment was found to be in the same areas.

Psychologically, even when separated and living in different environments, MZ twins may perform distinctive acts or make the same decisions at the same period in their lives.

A renowned German psychologist, Dr. Magnus Hirschfeld, also studied twins. Robert and Peter, identicals, were separated at seven by their parents' death. Robert went to prosperous relatives in Vienna, received a Ph.D. in physics, and became engaged to a wealthy girl. Then at the same age both twins met disaster in wild love affairs.

Robert became hopelessly infatuated with a prostitute and soon married her. His family and the university washed their hands of him, and when he could find no work, his wife went back to the streets to keep him. He wound up a derelict. Peter, a happily married businessman, also deserted his wife for a similar woman of lush proportions. After becoming a hopeless alcoholic he was jailed as a thief.[3]

The French army had two extraordinary sets of identical twin generals. The eighteenth-century Fauscher twins' promotions, wounds, and honors occurred simultaneously until they rolled over the cobblestones in the same cart to the guillotine. In World War I Generals Theodore and Felix Bret had near-identical records. Their handwriting was so alike that they were suspected of cheating in military school. After the war they topped the story by marrying, at forty-one, identical twins.

We quote English writer Harvey Day's "Linked Lives" for the story of twin dancers Jean and "Joe" Readinger.

> They sometimes had to separate but nothing could separate their minds. Once when Jean was in Chicago she thought out an intricate dance routine which everyone said was highly original.
>
> In Pittsburgh, 600 miles away, "Joe" thought out exactly the same complicated dance steps, and when they met one would have thought they had been practicing the same routine together for months.

This sympathetic rapport between twins can even include life's final event—death. So strongly forged can be the link between them that one follows the other in a short time.

In January, 1956, a report from Marseilles, France, told the strange story of a young British seaman, seventeen-year-old Michael Chillsom, on the merchant ship *Alhama*. He had a twin brother, Alex, hundreds of miles away in Steps, Scotland. Alex died on New Year's Day, and when Michael received the news, he succumbed to the same ailment, dying within forty-eight hours of his brother.[4]

The story of "the quiet men of Dunkirk" is especially touching. Jean and Yves Delavance, thirty-nine-year-old twin brothers, led such inseparable lives that they even managed to stay in the same work camp in Germany during World War II.

When they were released after the war, their parents died. They reopened the family grocery store and continued to wait on customers in identical gray sweaters and trousers.

In 1954 Yves fell in love, but he did not marry the girl.

"To have real happiness my brother and I ought to marry twin sisters," he said. "We are still children in need of each other. I will not marry because I do not want to leave my brother."

When Yves fell ill and died, holding his twin's hand, Jean was so grief-stricken that he was hospitalized on the day of the funeral.

Doctors could find nothing wrong, but he, too, passed away a week later.

"It's very strange," said his doctor. "But apparently he simply could not live without his twin. I suppose you would say that he died of sorrow."[5]

The Simultaneous-Death Phenomenon

Even more astonishing are the deaths that occur almost simultaneously without either twin knowing of the other's passing.

> On December 24, 1960, at 3:58 p.m. Arthur Bruce Cochran died in the U.S. Marine Hospital at Staten Island, New York. Within two hours his sister received a telegram from a hospital in California, saying that Arthur's twin brother, Albert, *whom he had not seen for over ten years,* had died at 1:03 Pacific Standard Time—less than six minutes apart![6]

Another such case occurred near Helsinki, Finland, in December, 1970. The parents of identical twin sisters, Tuula and Marjatta Jaavaara, said, "They always did the same things. Sometimes they fell ill at the same time, even if separated."

They were twenty-three years old, apparently in fine health. But right after dinner on this winter evening Tuula complained that she felt dizzy and sick.

As her father, Eino Jaavaara, put her in the car for a hurried trip to the hospital, Marjatta came downstairs from the room the twins shared. When told what had happened, she, too, became dizzy and collapsed. "Take care of Tuula. I'll be all right," she assured them.

She never spoke again. An ambulance got her to the hospital at about the same time as Tuula arrived in her father's car. External heart massage and other efforts failed. The girls remained in a coma, and less than an hour after arrival they both died within ten minutes of each other.

"We have no explanation as yet," said Dr. Klaus Runeberg, the hospital's senior physician. "One has heard about telepathic links between identical twins, but a case like this seems incredible." Post-mortem examinations were made, but no explanation was found beyond the original one of heart failure.

A close friend of ours has given us another strange story of dual deaths for twin brothers. The precise date and the names have gone from her memory, but it happened near her Florida home and in the year of her son's birth, 1934. The twins, whom we will call Charles and Arthur Davis, were between thirty and forty, and both were high-school teachers (one, she thinks, was a principal) in the areas surrounding Daytona Beach and Miami.

Florida has very heavy rainfall, and in those Depression years of poor highways, after a flash rain the sides of the roads were often brimming like lakes clear up over the berm.

On the day of the accidents both men were driving alone—Charles along the highway between Deland and Daytona Beach, and Arthur many miles farther south out of Miami. Both cars were wrecked on the rain-drowned roads, both men were flung clear of their cars, and both were found face down in the water, so that they may have died of drowning rather than their other injuries.

Apparently here again we have twins who were simultaneously programmed for death.

The next case is especially startling because of the very long separation between the brothers and their probable lack of contact. A London cab driver named Jonathan Meeras, fifty-eight years old, died on April 18, 1961, of a sudden heart attack with no previous illness. A few days later an astonishing letter came to his address. It stated that his identical twin, Arthur, had also died on April 18, in Freetown, Sierra Leone, Africa. The brothers had been separated for thirty-four years![7]

Even more eerie is the tale of twins who committed murder in different cities at the same time. On July 19, 1958, a twenty-one-year-old laborer stood before the judge in New Rochelle, New York, accused of the murder of a drifter. At the very same time in Mount Vernon, New York, his twin brother was arrested for killing the operator of a junkyard in a quarrel over a dog. Both of the murdered victims were thirty-six years old.[8]

Perhaps the grimmest and most sensational story of dual deaths occurred some years ago in a southern prison. Twin brothers were serving time there—Gene Trumbull and Bill Moddox, the latter an assumed name. Trumbull was awaiting execution for murder. Moddox faced a fifty-year stretch for armed robbery and was an electrician in the power plant of the penitentiary.

Via the prison grapevine he had been sending desperate messages to the death cell promising his brother that he would somehow "fix it."

But the hour for the death walk came without any external evidence that Moddox would be able to effect any "miracle," and Trumbull moved along with the guards and clergyman to his doom. Then, as the warden read the death warrant, the lights winked out.

"Take him back to his cell. Something has gone wrong!" the warden ordered.

Coincidence? No. In this old-style penitentiary the power for the electric chair came only from the prison plant. A week earlier when Moddox oiled the generator, he had added emory dust, hoping to burn out the bearings. On the morning of the execution during the increasing tension of preparation, he noticed that the bearings had begun to smoke. But would they burn out in time?

As the hour approached, he snatched up a huge crowbar and heaved it into the whirling flywheel. The flywheel boomeranged the crowbar back at him, pinning him to the big knife switch that controlled the power.

When the guards arrived a few minutes later, Moddox was dead from the charge that would have killed his brother—who was himself executed shortly thereafter in accordance with his sentence.[9]

Death from Within?

There is a dismaying duality, profoundly mysterious, in the lives and deaths of Bobbie Jean and Betty Jo Eller, identical twins of Purlear, North Carolina. As reported by Doctors Ian C. Wilson and John C. Reece in the *Archives of General Psychiatry* (October, 1964), the girls were linked with such an extreme togetherness, so great a neurosis, that they were destroyed.[10]

They were born on August 19, 1930, as triplets, but their tiny brother lived only an hour. As they grew up, they shared childhood diseases, toothaches, and identical clothing.

As teen-agers a slight change came; Bobbie, both physically and mentally, was beginning to pull ahead of Betty. Instead of becoming truly individuals, however, their twinship rapport continued but with Bobbie becoming the dominant one. The class of 1949 named Bobbie as the graduate most likely to succeed.

There was no noticeable tension between the twins. Betty simply imitated the dominant Bobbie, wearing glasses when Bobbie did, although she didn't need them, and discarding them when Bobbie did. After graduation they separated for the first time when Bobbie took a job in a variety store ten miles away. But after a year Bobbie came home. They went to Winston-Salem, North Carolina, to work together at the R. J. Reynolds Tobacco Company.

Suddenly madness crept into their deep partnership. Bobbie was the first victim. As usual, the twins came home one weekend from Winston-Salem. It was obvious that something was wrong with Bobbie. She wept, stared into space, and apparently didn't hear the words addressed to her. Her parents kept her home. Betty tried to continue working to maintain independence but had to return to Purlear.

Within weeks Betty was drawn into the vortex of mental illness that had absorbed her twin. They retreated to their room when visitors came. As they plummeted deeply into their twinned selves, they were finally admitted to the Broughton State Mental Hospital at Morgantown.

Briefly released several times, they were finally put on special drugs in January, 1962, to be administered at home. But the drugs meant a return to reality, so they refused to take the medication. At times, they had to be fed by force.

On April 11, thin and hardly aware of the real world, they were brought back to the hospital. Psychiatrists decided that Bobbie's domination of Betty was aggravating their illness.

Accordingly, that night they were separated—their first physical separation since they had been stricken—and tranquilizers were administered after both suffered catatonic seizures at the same time. About 11 P.M. Betty asked for a glass of water. At 12:55 A.M. the nurse in Bobbie's room suddenly realized that Bobbie wasn't breathing. Bobbie was dead. Immediately the nurse called the ward where Betty was sleeping and asked for a checkup. Betty was found lying on the floor beside her bed, dead. Both were lying in the same fetal position, on their right sides, legs drawn up.

Autopsies were performed by Dr. John C. Reece, former president of the State Medical Society and the North Carolina Pathological Society. Suicide was ruled out for many reasons.

"I found no demonstrable evidence of injury or disease that could cause death," he reported in bewilderment.

A thorough analysis of the twins' vital organs for possible drug poisoning was made by experts at the state's Bureau of Investigation. All tests were negative. The organs were then sent to the FBI in Washington. They, too, could find no cause of death.

Instead, death had seemingly come from within them, from their minds and the realm of fantasy they shared. Perhaps they had somehow acquired the power to die at will. If so, did the answer lie in Bobbie's dominance? Did Bobbie, dying, take her twin with her, silently commanding Betty to follow her still?

"They were like two people with one brain," their family physician said. "And that brain was in Bobbie."

Twins and Reincarnation

Today there is a growing interest in the possibility of reincarnation, not only in popular books but in the papers of sober scientists. Here are three cases of children who are supposed to have returned to life as twins.

The first was investigated by Dr. Ian Stevenson, the distinguished Alumni Professor of Psychiatry at the University of Virginia's School of Medicine. After years of conventional research and writing, he began to investigate reincarnation, because he felt that neither heredity nor environment accounted for some life histories.

Dr. Stevenson writes as follows:

> I have myself studied most extensively the evidence from cases of the reincarnation type. I have some data on almost six hundred such cases consisting mostly of the experiences of people who claim that they can remember having lived before. These claims have varying merits, and some cases are clearly richer and more authentic than others. I am satisfied myself, however, that for many of the cases I have studied, reincarnation is the best explanation I can find today for these particular cases.[11]

One of his recent cases appeared in an article entitled "Is There a Life after Death?" by Eugene Kinkead in *Look* magazine, October 20, 1970. It involves an identical twin named Gail Habbyshaw in Mercer, Pennsylvania.

Gail is small for her eighteen years, brunette, and friendly. Although her Christian family cannot explain it, she has been attracted to the Jewish religion since childhood. Finally, she quit going to

Sunday school and on Saturdays is driven some fifteen miles to the nearest synagogue to attend the Jewish service.

Convinced that she was killed by the Nazis in Germany in another life, she is now converting to Judaism. Her sister Susan has no interest in the matter at all and enjoys pork and shellfish, which revolt Gail. Dr. Stevenson talked to both Gail and her mother and found that their testimony agreed on all points. The twins' genetic and environmental backgrounds are the same. Yet their religious inclinations and personalities are very different.

Dr. Stevenson is a cautious scientist who recognizes at least seven other explanations (besides fraud) for his many cases. He continues to investigate with scrupulous objectivity the stories that come to him from correspondents all over the world.

Our second case is older and has been discussed by such eminent and sober psychical researchers as Charles Richet, René Warcollier, and others not given to fictionalization.[12]

Alexandrina was the five-year-old daughter of Dr. Carmelo Samona, a prominent physician in Palermo, Sicily. On March 15, 1910, the little girl died. In a vivid dream her distraught mother heard the child say, "Do not cry anymore! I have not left you for good. I will come back again, little, like this," and dramatically her tiny fingers flicked off a minute speck.

Three days later the dream recurred. Signora Samona told it to a friend, who lent her a book on reincarnation. But the mother said she couldn't accept such nonsense. Besides, doctors thought she could not even conceive, let alone bear a child, since her operation following a miscarriage the year before.

However, after the family heard three loud knocks and found no one there, they held a séance. By this means a strange story gradually unfolded—one that could easily be dismissed as pure wishful thinking if it were not for the events that happened during the following eight or nine years.

Their two communicators claimed to be the child herself and a sister of Dr. Samona's who had died long before at the age of fifteen. Over and over the message came: "Little mother, don't cry anymore. I shall be born once more with you as my mother, and before Christmas I'll be with you again!"

In mid-April Signora Samona began to believe that she might be pregnant, and by May she was sure. The communicator now said,

"Mother, there is another one as well within you." The "aunt" then broke in to say that another entity who wanted to return to earth was hovering about, and from then on the child kept insisting with great joy that she was going to come back with a little sister.

The Samonas were growing very upset. The whole idea outraged the doctor's scientific mind and his wife's religious beliefs. Also, there had been no twins on either side of the family, and her delicate health made them doubt that even one child could be born alive. But a well-known gynecologist, Dr. Vincent Cordaro, expressed a cautious belief that there might be twins in her womb.

At the next séance the announcement came that Alexandrina could not communicate again, since after the third month she would be more and more enveloped in material conditions and would enter a state of sleep.

On November 22 nonidentical twin daughters were born. They named the smaller Alexandrina, and as she matured, she grew astonishingly like her namesake with the same disposition, likes, dislikes, and speech idiosyncracies. As the likenesses grew, Dr. Samona wrote the particulars to his fellow physicians and to the editors of various newspapers.

The twin sisters were totally different, but Alexandrina II grew more and more like the dead child. She cared nothing for dolls but enjoyed tidying her room and arranging clothing in neat piles. She was also left-handed.

But most astonishing of all was the occasion of a family outing when the twins were about eight years old. They were all going to visit an ancient Norman cathedral at Monreale.

Immediately Alexandrina spoke up and said that she remembered Monreale. When her parents said she had never been there, she insisted they were wrong.

"Oh, yes, I went there! Don't you remember, there was a great church with a very large statue of a man with his arms held open, on the roof? And don't you remember we went there with a lady who had horns and that we met some little red priests in the town?"

Signora Samona was stunned to recall that they had taken the first Alexandrina to Monreale with a lady who had prominent growths on her forehead. Before they entered the old church they had met a group of Greek priests whose robes were decorated with red.

This whole story was formally attested in print in the greatest detail by several well-known people of Palermo, including a Protestant minister and several members of the nobility who knew the family well.

The following case was also investigated by Dr. Ian Stevenson, but since he has not yet released his information on it, our data come from other sources.

The children involved are still young, and they seemingly remember the day they "died." One Sunday in May, 1957, in the little town of Hexham, Northumberland, England, eleven-year-old Joanna and six-year-old Jacqueline Pollock were on their way to Mass. As they skipped along in high spirits, a car shot around the corner of the narrow country lane and smashed into them. Both children were killed.

The Pollocks were dazed with grief. They were quiet, simple, religious people. Mr. Pollock was a milkman at the time. On his route he thought about it constantly. Finally about a year later he astounded his pregnant wife by saying he was certain that both the girls were coming back to them as twins.

So insistent was his notion about twins that a week before her confinement Mrs. Pollock consulted a doctor. He detected only one heartbeat and one fetus, so she went home in triumph to announce that James's hunch was all hogwash.

But he won after all. Seventeen months after the tragedy twin girls were actually born to them. They named them Gillian and Jennifer, and in their delight it really did seem that they had their own girls back again.

Soon odd things began to happen. The family moved to Whitley Bay, and there, while rummaging in the attic one day, Mr. Pollock found a box of toys that had belonged to the dead children, never untied since their death.

When he unpacked it, Jennifer snatched up a doll and cried, "Daddy! Here's my Mary!" and Gillian recognized a toy clothes wringer as her own. It had been Joanna's favorite toy.

On another occasion while doing some painting Mr. Pollock put on an old smock of his wife's. It was one she had worn years before when she went to pick up Joanna and Jacqueline at their school. It, too, had been stored away.

Immediately Jennifer cried, "Why, Daddy, why are you wearing Mommy's school coat?"

You can say that a gullible father, eager for a romantic tale, has "fed" some of this information to the children unconsciously, but surely not all of it, especially when they now call by name visitors who come from out of town whom they have never met—in this life.

Another time a neighbor found them crying at the corner where the accident had occurred. They asked her, "What happened to Mr. ——? Is he still upset about the crash?" They not only knew the name of the man responsible but the kind of vehicle he drove.

There are strange physical similarities, too. Jennifer was born with an odd white scar on her forehead, the same size and in the same position as one little Jacqueline had received in a fall three years before she died. Gillian, too, has a red-brown birthmark on her hip, just as their oldest girl had had.

Strangely, such likenesses in scars and birthmarks are often noted in reincarnation cases. When they occur with two children, however, the enigma becomes even more uncanny.

7 THE FABULOUS MULTIPLES—
TRIPS, QUADS, AND QUINTS

The cute little blonde in her flowered shortie tossed in the panic of a nightmare. This wasn't a giant hippopotamus trampling her. The hippo was *inside* her!

Shirley sat upright and looked with terror at the dim form of her sleeping husband. "This isn't just Chuck, Jr.!" she said accusingly to his oblivious back. "This has got to be twins!"

As a matter of fact, it was not twins. It was triplets. Shirley learned the startling truth next day when she went to the Oakland, California, Naval Hospital on the base where her husband, Chief Petty Officer Charles N. Niehoff, was stationed at the time. She was already seven months pregnant. When the doctor told her she must get to bed and stay there, she was just plain scared. They now had two boys still in diapers. Soon there would be *five* babies.

As an only child who had never even baby-sat, Shirley had found the two previous babies unfamiliar enough. Fortunately her husband, from a big family, loved children—but she was the one having the triplets.

Actually, without the navy and its hospital facilities she would have lost the triplets. For how else could a wife in modest circumstances afford two whole months in bed? Thanks to the navy the entire bill for the two months' hospitalization plus delivery was a mere one hundred dollars.

"Charles kidded me that it cost him more to keep me in cigarettes and secondhand paperbacks than the hospital charged!" she told us.

There had been twins on both sides of the family—always fraternals on her side and identicals on his. But three at once—that was something else again. However, her two months in bed were not all occupied with worrying about how to cope.

The afternoons were enlivened by "triplet-watching." Kept on a low sodium diet, Shirley lost tissue fluid so rapidly that it was possible to see the babies' tiny knuckles through the flesh of her abdomen. Before the evening meal the triplets seemed to roll around merrily, so the nurses came in relays to watch the gymnastics in the womb.

Since she had had polio years before, a spinal block was forbidden. She wanted no anesthetics, for she and the navy doctors believed that the last three or four breaths the mother takes are vitally important for the emerging baby's future health. With triplets especially, and in so small a mother, they needed all the oxygen possible during the process.

The doctors were wrong on one point; they had expected two-to-three-pound infants. Actually each girl averaged five pounds. The last was a breech birth, but by that time dilation of the cervical canal was sufficient to cause no problem. Of the three, Veronica and Cindy were identicals, probably a couple of weeks premature, and the firstborn, Teresa—heavier, better developed, and with lots of hair—was more like a full-term child.

Because the little ones at home had colds, the new babies stayed at the hospital for a few days. The week after they were all together, Shirley came back from her first real trip out of the house laden with Christmas shopping. Immediately young John began looking anxiously into all the bags.

"No baby this time, Mommy?" And when she laughed and shook her head, a beaming smile spread over his face. "Oh—all done! Just two for us and one for Mommy and Daddy!"

Occasionally multiples arrive like shelling peas. One twenty-four-year-old mother in New York had all her triplets within three minutes.

Mrs. Feenie Ziner tells of the birth of her daughter, who arrived "with an honor guard of two brothers to protect her," as she put it. Her babies did not require incubators. In her account, "The Day the Triplets Came," she says:

The hospital confirmed what I had known from the moment I first set eyes upon the triplets—that no two of them were identical. . . . In other words, each of them had developed from a separate egg.

Being a nondescript cook, I took special pleasure in having, for once in my life, made *these* eggs just right![1]

Frequency of Multiples

When we come to these bigger multiples, the "supertwins," what are the chances? Many premature infants who would once have died are saved today, and the twins among them will tend to have more twins. Nevertheless, aside from the fertility drugs, according to national vital statistics, there has been some decline in the frequency of multiple births.

"Hellin's rule," adopted by a German scientist of that name in 1895, involved the ratio of twin and supertwin births. His figures indicated that the number of triplets would be the square of the ratio of twins to singletons; for quads, the cube of the ratio; and for quints, he carried the figure to the fourth power. This, however, is only an approximation.

According to studies made by the Department of Health, Education, and Welfare in 1964, the ratio of twins to total deliveries for all races was 1:96. From this the frequency expected for triplets is 1:9,216, and the actual frequency about 8 percent less. On the other hand, the actual frequency of quads (1:663,470) was 33 percent higher than was expected.

Since the 1920's there has been some decline in the frequency of multiples with each decade. H.E.W.'s figures for 1964—which of course do not cover the drug multiples—are lower than the 1950's, as that decade was lower than the 1940's.

As already stated, Negro mothers have more multiples, and Orientals fewer, than whites, and the rapid admixture of races could dilute the genetic tendencies. For both whites and blacks the more live births a woman has, the more likely she is to bear twins. The proportion of identicals to fraternals is not the same for all races, blacks having about 10 percent more fraternals.

These statistics are for normal births. The new drugs will change the figures.

According to Scheinfeld, there are probably no more than 250 to 300 surviving sets of triplets annually among the United States's six million births; and the country's total number, including adults, is only about 10,000.[2] With quadruplets the country has never averaged one living set per year, although there may be five or six sets, of whom some are stillborn. Perhaps a dozen sets of all ages survive across the United States.

Quadruplets

All identicals are quite rare among quadruplets. The Morlok girls, born May 19, 1930, in Lansing, Michigan, and the Hargreave girls in 1949 were unique at that time. The Keys girls of Hollis, Oklahoma, born in 1915, comprised two identicals and two fraternals. They became famous as the first quads to go through college—Baylor University in Texas. Of these girls the identical pair was very much alike, whereas the two fraternal sisters differed markedly from each other as well as from the other two.

The Schenses, an all-fraternal set of two boys and two girls, were born January 13, 1931, in Hecla, South Dakota, as different from each other as any siblings. Another set, the Perricone boys, born in Texas in 1929, were also from four different eggs and quite different physically.

On June 1, 1968, a Hawaiian couple—Carol and Kenneth Villaros —in Culver City, California, had what the father called "an easy and beautiful experience." During the fourth month of Carol's pregnancy X rays revealed four little bodies in her womb, but she took the news in stride. For several weeks after birth the babies—all boys and two months premature—were kept in incubators.

Villaros, employed at an aluminum plant in Torrance, was overcome to learn that his company's health-insurance plan would pay the huge hospital costs—somewhere between $8,500 and $10,000—and a baby-food company would provide food for a year.

"What a country!" he said. "We didn't plan a large family, it just happened—for the best, that's for sure." Married six years, they had a three-year-old girl, Stefanie, when the quads arrived.

"What will you do when all four boys are old enough to ask for the car at once?" a reporter asked.

"I hope they'll like to double-date!" Villaros told him.

The Axe family of Lima, Ohio, always wanted a houseful of kids. After three pregnancies Barbara announced that one of her "signs" was having a glass pitcher smash into smithereens. So when in August, 1962, the iced tea spattered in a shower of glass, she said jokingly that she hardly needed to go to the doctor.

But unlike her earlier pregnancies, she needed maternity clothes by the third month and was so immense that the doctor thought she had miscalculated. A nurse herself, Barbara was working in the operating room two nights a week in spite of her size.

Then shortly after X rays taken in February revealed four tiny spines, her doctor was hospitalized. Rueful at his own bad luck in missing a spectacular birth, he said, "I feel the way John Glenn would if he'd forgotten to get in his satellite!"

The first two babies arrived within two minutes, and when the third took eleven, one of the obstetricians joked that maybe Barbara could leave for a coffee break. All four identical girls arrived within seventeen minutes—two of them weighing more than four pounds and the tiniest a little better than two.

Because C.B.S. flew Barbara and Phil to "I've Got a Secret," and they received much local publicity and some gifts, townspeople thought Phil had it made. But the newspaper that employed him soon failed, and he had to move alone to Toledo. When they were finally able to relocate together, they still had to keep up payments on their Lima house.

Six months later Phil was hopefully approaching advertisers for television contracts when the Fischer quints were born—and mere quads became obsolete! Aside from a new car, free diaper service, and milk, their bonanza totaled little more than fifteen hundred dollars. Phil confessed wryly that he was not quitting work and that it's possible to be a loser with four aces.[3]

The Dionne Quintuplets

As for five at a time, it is unlikely that any babies will ever surpass the Dionne quintuplets in rarity. They are the only *one*-egg set ever recorded, and thus by their long survival (Emilie died in 1954 and Marie in 1970) they still constitute the world's most remarkable birth. The new fertility-drug multiples, which always come from separate eggs, cannot rival them.

They arrived inconspicuously very early on May 28, 1934, in a primitive Canadian farmhouse—and life for their parents was never the same again.

Dr. Allan Dafoe, summoned from sleep at 4 A.M., arrived to find two babies already warming by the fire. From the first he insisted that the five girls were identicals and was convinced that they were originally six, not five. Support for his belief is given by the fact that Mrs. Dionne had labor pains in the third month and passed a black object similar to a duck egg—presumably an embryonic mass—which may have been Cecile's twin partner.

Control of the babies was promptly taken out of family hands. Papa Dionne in his upheaval had signed a contract when they were only three days old to exhibit them at the Chicago Century of Progress. To prevent such exploitation, they were made wards of King George V. A trust fund was set up, and the girls were kept under strict supervision in a nine-room nursery built across the road.

There were fourteen on the payroll with a guard making the rounds at night. The quints seldom saw their parents, and Papa Dionne was reprimanded when he tried to take a picture of his own babies through the window. All rights to picture-taking had been sold to a news bureau.

Antagonism built up between Papa Dionne and Dr. Dafoe, who came daily in his coonskin coat and otter cap. Eventually the family succeeded in moving the quints into the new, elaborate "Big House" they had built from the trust fund, but it was too late to establish family harmony. The girls were not happy because the older children resented them, and they were given heavy work to do.

Eventually the quints were sent to live in a convent school, where Emilie, the frailest, began to suffer epileptic seizures. Eventually she became a nun. She was found dead in bed one morning in August, 1954, the victim of an unattended convulsion.

The other girls took an apartment together in Montreal. One by one, Cecile, Marie, and Annette fell in love and married. Yvonne became a nun. The three who married have had children of their own, all singletons except Cecile's. But of her twin boys, one died at fifteen months. Marie separated from her husband, and on February 27, 1970, she died, leaving two little girls. Only Annette is still married.

The Quints of Argentina

The world's next set of quintuplets arrived secretly in Buenos Aires on July 15, 1943. Their birth was a mystery. All kinds of rumors sprang up. Some thought they were the children of two mothers, and for a long time doctors would not accept the real story. It seemed too incredible that secretly—unpublicized for eight months—five tiny infants could have survived without incubators or doctors, even in a luxurious environment. But they did.

The fact that their father was a millionaire made both the secrecy and the survival possible.

Señor Franco Diligenti had arrived in Argentina as a poor Italian boy and built up a great fortune in textiles and vegetable oils. He married an opera singer, Ana Aversano, who had had two children by a former marriage. After becoming his wife she had lost triplets in the second month of pregnancy. Another pregnancy did not disturb her, and she remained well and active until the last few weeks.

Like many Latin mothers, she disliked examination by a male physician and chose a third-generation midwife with facilities in her home. Several months before, Mrs. Delfino had told her, "This will not be a solo. There is a whole orchestra in there!"

But Señora Diligenti refused to be perturbed. In her family there had been plenty of twins and triplets!

On July 15 a friend called Señor Diligenti at his factory to tell him that his wife had just given birth.

"Good news!" the millionaire said cheerfully. "Boy or girl?"

"Franco," the friend is reported to have answered, "try to retain your tranquillity. You have been dealt a full house. Three queens and a pair of jacks. You are the Papa Dionne of Argentina!"

There was a stunned and lengthy silence. "Por Dios!" Diligenti exclaimed hoarsely. At forty-five he had been planning to retire and become a world traveler with his beautiful wife. One child might not have disturbed these plans too much—but five?

Immediately the brain responsible for building a great industrial complex meshed into action. Not for him the fanfare and interference that had hounded the little Dionnes! He commanded the midwife to silence. The two tiniest infants, a boy and a girl, remained for four months at her home. The strongest boy and girl were registered as twins at one bureau and the remaining girl at another. The other two were not registered till the following April, although the correct date was given with the midwife's address.

But even in wealthy suburbs six nursemaids and many deliveries of supplies will cause gossip! The fact that the secret was kept for eight months is probably a record in itself. When the news broke, against

Diligenti's will, it is easy to see why doctors were suspicious after swarming reporters were not permitted to see the children. The facts outraged medical history.

Eventually, in the interests of science Diligenti decided that the story should be told by the midwife to Dr. Josué Beruti, who published it in medical journals with the statement that he accepted the facts given him by several witnesses as an accurate and exact account. "I also believe," he continued, "that my findings will refute those rumors which imply that this birth was not the birth of quintuplets."

It became clear that Señora Diligenti, after a fairly normal pregnancy, had had a very difficult confinement. On the afternoon of July 14 with her pains coming every thirty minutes, she arrived at the midwife's home.

Labor took nineteen and a half hours, but her naturally strong body recovered quickly, and the infants, though small, were not premature. All this, in far greater detail, appeared in Dr. Beruti's account.

After five days of lying-in, Señora Diligenti came home with the three strongest babies and not only breast-fed them (plus a supplementary bottle) but sent her extra milk to the little ones at Mrs. Delfino's. Thus all five babies received some mother's milk and gained steadily.

Nearly two years later a magistrate ruled on the charges for false registration of the births. However regrettable for science, he said, the father's desire to avoid notoriety was reasonable, and Dr. Beruti's report was accepted as fact. The five babies had had one mother and a very remarkable birth.

Commanding wealth and power, Señor Diligenti kept all publicity at a minimum. The quints flourished, but according to their unnerved father, confusion and clamor made the mansion "like a mechanic's pit in a car race."

He used his inventive genius to devise a five-seater potty-bench. "I may patent it someday, even though there is not much market for it!" he remarked. "They are like a little Mafia with their own secrets and loyalties."

He was fiercely determined that they would grow up as separate entities and was perturbed to detect "a certain psychic affinity" between at least two pairs. To foil this he enrolled all five children in different schools. But when Franco had a tooth pulled, Maria Cristina complained of toothache; and when Carlos broke his arm, Maria Ester's school called to say she was suffering from an inexplicable pain in that arm.

From then on the children were kept strictly apart, each in separate private schools, except for great fiestas on their birthday and special holidays. Yet within this framework they had liberty to choose their own lives, and Diligenti was delighted when they confused reporters deliberately with conflicting stories. They speak five languages and can and do cut Papa out with one he doesn't know!

At sixteen and eighteen two of the girls married while the third studied in Rome. Franco and Carlos enrolled in the University of British Columbia, choosing their own courses They remained a close group, constantly in touch by plane and letters.

"But whenever I get a letter from Vancouver," says Señor Diligenti, "I can expect to receive one from Maria Cristina in Italy, written on the same day. They are still as alike as two drops of water."[4]

The Quints Who Broke the Odds

Although the odds are said to be 54,000,000 to 1, in September, 1963—twenty-nine years after the Dionnes—*two* sets of quintuplets were born into an astonished world. The first set arrived in Venezuela, the second in Aberdeen, South Dakota. From the beginning, Inez Cuervo Prieto, wife of an oil driller on Lake Maracaibo, Venezuela, knew that this pregnancy was different. She was thirty-four, mother of five, and already a grandmother, but the clinic insisted her excessive size and nausea only meant that she had miscalculated. In great misery she finally consulted a midwife.

"But there is something miraculous here, little daughter!" the astonished woman said. "I can feel the flutter of many wings!"

Next day the midwife took Inez to a bigger clinic, where X rays confirmed the staggering fact of quints. In a few days Inez was sent to the University Hospital in Maracaibo, close enough for her husband, Efren, and her children to visit her. Although she was almost immobilized in bed for a full month and miserable from the constant kicking of the babies within her, the gentleness and good care she received assuaged her fright.

The doctors had counted on a cesarean, but Inez said, "The babies did not know the doctors' plans. They had chosen their own time and the giving of light had come." Over a period of fifty minutes five tiny boys were born, with their mother conscious and calm the whole time.

"At least let out a yelp!" one nurse pleaded. "So we know you are having a baby!"

"But I felt no need to cry out," Inez explained later. "There was not more pain than I could bear."

All that day Efren Prieto had been uneasy, but the boss would not give him the day shift. Before he could leave work, the excitement was countrywide, and Venezuela's President was phoning twice a day.

Efren wept when he went to see his wife, and when she told him the births had been easy and accomplished without a cesarean, he confessed, "I cried again for happiness, for I had feared they would cut her."

Reporters swarmed around as he left. "What do you eat that makes you get five babies at once?" they wanted to know.

In his joy Efren had a bit of fun. "I eat only fish," he told one, and another, "Only oxtail soup"—which he doesn't much like.

Next day the butchers had sold all their oxtails.

All the previous months he and Inez had been in great dismay, for the ten dollars a day he earned helped to support ten children of his own and four of Inez's from other unions. But now responsibility faded as a foundation—"F5V," Fundación Quintuples Venezolanos, made up of doctors, social workers, and civil leaders—was set up and a new house given them. The whole country was ecstatic, and donations poured in.

But a week later national shock was severe when the Fischer quints arrived in South Dakota.

"The North Americans, who do not like to stay behind in anything, have had quintuplets too!" the local newspaper moaned. "We Venezuelans were not given time fully to savor the fruits of our colossal success. But one distinction remains ours alone—they are all boys!"

The sturdy babies were in incubators only part of the time. Their parents watched them through the nursery window and were sometimes permitted to give them their bottles. But Inez grieved that she was not allowed to nurse them.

"But I do not complain," she said. "For I have given my husband five sons at once, what no woman in the world has ever done before, and they are all alive and well. And that for me is happiness enough!"

A year later the Prietos had had many problems but had come out of them well. Since Efren is a simple man, he was exploited by a lawyer who, when the foundation to "help" the Prietos was dissolved, emerged with most of the cash. But the Creole Petroleum Company, Efren's employers, then moved them into a five-bedroom, thirty-thousand-dollar house where they can live rent-free until the babies reach twenty-one. Then it will become their property, so the parents are actually the children's guests. Even if Efren quits his job, the house is secured to them, and they will still be entitled to medical care and schooling at company expense.

Once established in this comfortable home, Inez even suggested to Efren that he bring eight of his other children there. "Where there is room for ten, there is room for twenty," she said placidly.

Lined up in a row behind the pink concrete wall by Inez each afternoon, like little bronze idols, they are proudly displayed for the community to enjoy. Efren became "a father of fathers," immensely proud of his sons and helping faithfully with their care.[5]

The Year of the Multiples

By a strange stroke of fate, 1963 might be called the Year of the Multiples, with two Saturdays in September its peak. In March Barbara Axe had her quads; in June the Negro Harris quads arrived; and on Saturday, September 7, and Saturday, September 14, two sets of quads and two sets of quints were born in far-flung corners of the world.

On the first date the Prietos had their boy quints, and Mrs. Thomas P. Harkins in Jackson, Mississippi, had four girls. On the fourteenth came the Fischer quints in Aberdeen, South Dakota, and also a set of quads in Iran. There, Kakhri Mousavi, wife of a shopkeeper named Mojtaba Rafieyan, had two boys and two girls in a town about three hundred miles south of Tehran.[6]

The Fischer quints were born two months ahead of schedule to parents who already had five children. Mrs. Fischer admits to having cried all night when told her X rays revealed five more. They were already having a hard time financially in a rented farmhouse, with Andrew getting up at five to care for livestock before he went to his modest job.

"For two days after the news, I was like a mechanical man!" he said. "How could we ever take care of so many!" Oppressed by worry, it never occurred to either of them that like the Dionnes, they would receive help from outside sources.

The Fischer quints are not drug babies. They happened normally. Of the one boy and four girls who comprise the set two of the girls are identicals.

Where the Dionnes were popped into butcher baskets and placed on the door of the range, twenty-nine years later the Fischer babies had air-conditioned Isolettes and were fed through plastic tubes in the nose—about a teaspoon every two hours. "Preemies" lose less weight by evaporation if the humidity and temperature are kept high with small amounts of oxygen added.

The Fischers didn't call them the quints, but "the babies"—which includes the singleton, Cindy, born a year and ten days after "the five." According to their mother, Cindy was the best thing that could have happened, diverting attention from the celebrities so they were no longer the center of the stage and balancing the act so that the five previous children don't feel left out.

Even with all the labor-saving conveniences given them by the public, eleven children, eight hundred acres, and a huge herd of fine cattle make fantastic demands on energy. Somehow Mrs. Fischer manages a huge and thriving garden, planting by the moon like her own mother, but they no longer keep milk cows. She does have household help, and the five older children are trained to be useful. A cheerful, realistic woman who manages with phenomenal efficiency, she is always annoyed by the constant query "How do you do it?"

"Well, what do you *expect* I'm going to do?" she feels like retorting. "I put up with it, that's what I do. What choice have I? It's a lot of work but a lot of fun, too."

The town of Aberdeen had hoped to be put on the map by their quints, but it did not benefit financially the way Callandar, Ontario, did from the Dionnes, who raised their town's tourist income to one million dollars. No pictures of the babies are for sale, and about all the publicity comes from simple road signs reading, "Aberdeen, Home of the Fischer Quintuplets." The chamber of commerce wanted to build their fine new house, but the Fischers preferred to go heavily into debt to finance it themselves.[7]

They are luckier than the Dionnes. Jimmie, Cathy, Margie, little Mary Ann, and Maggie—"the five"—and now little Cindy, are growing up normally. Their common-sense rearing and older siblings who are not jealous and hostile have them headed for happiness without the blaze of publicity and family dissension that hounded the first quints.

South Africa then made the news with "natural" quints when on February 6, 1966, three boys and two girls arrived in East London. They were born to Tafeni Tukutese, a coal-yard worker earning just over eleven dollars a week, and his wife, Nogesi. The children probably set a record for sturdiness, with their combined weight of twenty-three pounds eight ounces, which is almost certainly the tops for quints.

The five births took one hour and seven minutes, and shortly after it was all over their mother scribbled down colorful names for her babies. The first boy was to be Kululekile ("Happy"); the second, Tembekile ("Trusted"); and the third, Mbambile ("I've Got It"). The little girls were Zoleka ("Serenity") and Tandeka ("Well-Beloved").

As if to confirm the good fortune in these happy-sounding names, the family circumstances improved. Because of poverty, the mother and oldest boy were living with a grandmother at a distance, while Father Tukutese shared with his father a shack so small that he said, "When I am in bed and my father is sleeping on the floor, there is no room for anyone else."

A modest fund was set up to help the family. The community gave them, rent-free, two adjoining houses, four rooms altogether, and a newspaper provided a better job. A nurse was also appointed to help with the children, who judging from their photograph (in this book), are very cute babies.[8]

The Case for Sextuplets

In the first part of this century four cases of sextuplets were reported in the United States. Of these sets one child survived. She was born to Mrs. Philip Speichinger in Mendon, Missouri, on August 9, 1936. Her photograph as an adult appears in the *Guinness Book of World Records,* 1963 edition.

Three children from a sextuplet birth in Michoacan, Mexico, on September 7, 1953, are reported to be still living. This is over a decade before the fertility drugs were in use, so they were conceived without the aid of hormones.

Eight sets of septuplets have been reported, but the drugless ones are not authenticated.

However, on March 12, 1967, United Press International reported octuplets—four boys and four girls—born to a twenty-one-year-old housewife in Mexico City. Weighing between ten and eleven *ounces* each, they were seven to eight inches long. After their birth in a private clinic they were rushed to the big government hospital, but one by one they died. It was not stated whether they were hormone babies.

Fertility-Drug Multiples

Now we come to the drug multiples of the mid-sixties. Whatever the number of these infants per birth, they can never be identicals— only fraternals—for the nature of these drugs is to stimulate production of separate eggs in the womb.

In the United States there are perhaps four million childless wives, of whom a large percentage seem to be miserable over their condition. But only a small number of them—the approximate 10 percent who suffer from subnormal functioning of the ovaries—can be helped by hormones. (In other cases the husband may be relatively sterile or the wife may have infected or malformed reproductive organs. Here other medical treatments, some very recently discovered, are available.)

Among those women who are infertile only because of a malfunctioning ovulation process, many develop a healthy egg monthly, but a lack of the proper hormones prevents it from being ejected into the fallopian tubes where the sperm can fertilize it.

Normally, at the beginning of the menstrual period, two tiny glands in or near the brain (the hypothalamus and the pituitary) control the secretion of two vital substances, which are called gonadotrophins because they are hormones that stimulate the gonads, or sex glands. One of these is the follicle-stimulating hormone (FSH), the other the luteinizing hormone (LH). Both are needed for the monthly release of an egg for fertilization. And as we know, multiple births result if this single egg divides or if more than one egg is released at a time.

The follicle is the nest in which the ovum lies on the surface of the ovary. FSH causes it to grow and to produce another hormone called estrogen. (There are always some follicles in the ovary producing estrogen, but most of it is made by the bigger follicles which are ripening the mature eggs.) The follicle begins to bulge during these changes, and usually on the fourteenth day of the menstrual cycle, it ruptures and lets the ovum drop into the fallopian tube.

The "pill" (estrogen) prevents the release of gonadotrophins by the pituitary. Hence FSH (and some LH) gets stored in the pituitary. When the "pill" is withdrawn, the bottled-up FSH is released, usually in excessive quantities at first, explaining why some women may then conceive multiples before a new equilibrium or feedback is established. Then normal rhythmic functions take place again.

The pioneer research on the fertility drugs themselves was done by Dr. Carl Gemzell, now at Uppsala, Sweden. The early drugs were variously produced, at first from animal pituitary glands, which caused unhappy side reactions. Next the pituitary was extracted from human bodies on the autopsy table, which required more than ten cadavers for one course of treatments.

Then Dr. Piero Donini, in Rome, discovered these gonadotrophins in the urine of women who had ceased to menstruate. Extracting human menopausal gonadotrophin (HMG) from urine volunteered by aging nuns, he made the drug pergonal. It causes the readying of two or more follicles and therefore of two or more eggs. Pergonal is mostly FSH and is much the same as pituitary FSH but, of course, more easily obtained.

A very interesting offshoot of this research was the discovery that pergonal would not only reverse female sterility but could also stimulate the production of sperm and thus reactivate male fertility. This is because all gonadotrophins work on both ovaries and testes— not on the germ cells themselves, but on surrounding cells. Stimulating the latter, the germ cells, in turn, are activated, and hormones are produced. This applies to FSH as well as to LH.

One might suggest that FSH may have been too hastily named "follicle-stimulating hormone," since there are no follicles in the testicles.

The third fertility drug, clomid, is synthetically produced. It is not a hormone, and how it can trigger ovulation is not completely understood. Presumably it works on the hypothalamus and through it stimulates the pituitary to produce FSH.

The results of these drugs vary with each woman and sometimes with the same woman at different times. The precise dosage seems also to be uncertain. Many of these patients have conceived an extraordinary number of fetuses at a time. Some of these children have been normal, some deformed or stillborn, and others soon died. There have also occasionally been toxic side effects on the mother— some of which, such as blurred vision, require cessation of the pill or injection. Some doctors have reported ovarian cysts.

They are tricky drugs, sometimes used in combination, and always demanding constant supervision. Now that doctors can measure the level of FSH in the blood (see Chapter 2), they believe they will be able to control the dosage to that the ovary will release only one or, at most, two eggs. But until this is certain, only the woman herself can decide whether the risk is worthwhile, and she may change her mind too late after a huge family becomes a reality.

As one father of quads—three girls and a boy—gasped, "Three weddings and four college educations! What am I going to do?" With such multibirths becoming more frequent, the early windfalls such as houses built by the community and lavish gifts are not always available to the parents.

Of the families who have successfully had multiples through drugs a New Zealand couple, Sam and Ann Lawson, of Auckland, are probably the happiest. Theirs was only the fifth set of surviving quints in history and the first to be conceived through the use of hormones.

Mrs. Lawson, twenty-six, had waited for five years for a companion for her daughter, Leanne. After enduring symptoms like the menopause she decided to try the drugs. Very soon she was pregnant. Her weight zoomed from 127 pounds to 193, and since her neck and limbs had become thin, the excess seemed to be entirely fetal weight of some 66 pounds.

Hospitalized well in advance, she managed cheerfully except for the discomfort of navigating her unwieldy body around the corridors. The sight of other women's preemies in the nursery unnerved her. They looked, she said, like tiny skinned rabbits, flesh taut over bones. Premature labor was halted; then on the night of July 26, 1965, the first drug quintuplets arrived in the world—one boy and four girls.

The boy and the biggest girl are dark, the other three, blondes. The babies are descendants of Fletcher Christian—of eighteenth-century *Mutiny on the Bounty* fame—who settled on Pitcairn Island in the South Pacific. The firstborn and the only boy among the quints is named Samuel Fletcher for his father and his famous ancestor.

The Lawsons, perhaps because of the fertility-drug factor, received a good deal of crank mail calling the babies freaks or making other unpleasant accusations. However, they were overjoyed by the babies' birth, especially as news of other dead or dying multiples began to be reported around the world.

The New Zealand Government, which has a remarkable health plan for citizens, assigned them two nurses and gave them two years' use of a hospital building they were planning to remodel. Here in a little flat above the nursery, on every fifth night she gave each quint, in turn, its own private feeding time alone with her. Like the Fischer quints of Aberdeen, South Dakota, these five seem likely to grow up as part of a happy family.

The United States soon followed the New Zealanders with more drug multiples. Several did not survive intact. Sheila and Herbert Sklar were among the fortunate ones. Sheila's menstrual cycle had always been irregular; finally she had a miscarriage, then a normal uncomplicated pregnancy followed by the old irregularity. When she decided to go to Columbia Presbyterian Medical Center in New York City for the drug treatment, she was given clomiphene citrate with the understanding that if it didn't work promptly, an operation would be necessary.[9]

However, she became pregnant immediately. Soon she suspected twins, then triplets—until finally X rays showed four! She, too, was forced by the enormous size of her body and great discomfort to go to the hospital in her sixth month.

Fortunately for the Sklars, the North Shore Hospital in Manhasset, Long Island, was uncommonly generous and exempted them from most charges. By means of the enforced bed rest (she soon could not even shift her own pillow or pick up her phone) she carried the babies well into the ninth month. On October 1, 1965, the actual birth was comparatively easy and quick. Three boys and a girl—nineteen pounds and six ounces of babies—arrived within six minutes.

During the following years childless wives besieged the doctors in this gamble with fate. A widely publicized case in Sweden resulted in seven stillbirths. A Boston woman also had seven who died soon after birth, and the same fate ended the pregnancy of a Belgian wife.

In Birmingham, England, Mrs. Sheila Thorns endured childlessness for ten years, then took gonadotrophin. On her own thirtieth birthday, October 2, 1968, she gave birth by cesarean section to sextuplets, and three survived. Because the National Health Service in England pays the cost, women there can assume the risk without the fear of being burdened for life by monstrous medical bills, but the other risks can hardly be considered minor.

Although doctors warn women that they may get more than they bargained for, it does not seem to stop them. And often enough to give them false confidence, the drugs do result in single births.

This happened to a mother in Rome. But on her second attempt, tragedy resulted. In July, 1971, she was rushed to the hospital in the fourth month of pregnancy. Doctors removed *fifteen* perfectly formed fetuses—ten girls and five boys—weighing about five ounces each, but all smothered in the womb.

With the Kienast quints of Liberty Corner, New Jersey, Peggy Kienast had also safely given birth to two singletons with the hormones. Her problem centered around the fact that she ceased to menstruate shortly after marriage because of a small pituitary tumor. (This is the gland that releases the hormones permitting pregnancy to occur.) Although treatment was successful, ovulation did not begin. But after daily injections of pergonal, she became pregnant with Meg, her first baby, then successfully repeated the injections with John.

But soon she was convinced that this third pregnancy was different —it was going to be twins. Because of a slight apprehension, however, she began firmly saying, "Think two!" But thinking two failed, for in mid-November X rays revealed four tiny skeletons and a shadow. She was soon very uncomfortable, although her babies didn't kick much. Perhaps they didn't have room!

She spent many weeks in bed at home, then was hospitalized in early January. Her abdomen was huge, "like a little Buddha," as one of her doctors said, and she was so uncomfortable that she snatched sleep an hour at a time.

However, on the night of February 24, 1970, the actual delivery required only ten minutes. Six weeks premature and all but one under four pounds, the five babies were kept in the hospital until April 27.

The hospital bill totaled $55,000!

Of this sum Bill Kienast expected his insurance to cover all but $800. Like the New Zealand Lawsons, they, too, received crank letters, but also many offers of help, especially through their church, which had a long list of members willing to do marketing and mending and even to tutor the babies when older. Kienast promptly hired a business manager and set up a trust fund for the babies. With four hundred diapers costing forty dollars a week, he was realist enough to know that television commercials would be useful.

They owned a five-room farmhouse, and local builders offered the labor for a big addition. But even with a visiting public-health nurse coming daily and a goodly number of friendly neighbors besides, the rearing of five quints and the two older children will require plenty of attention.

Probably in the next decade scientists will be able not only to control the number of these babies, but to improve their physique, mentality, and even their abilities.

Dr. E. S. E. Hafez, who as an experimental biologist at Washington State University is one of the world's leading researchers in the field, foresees startling possibilities, and very soon. He suggests, reports David M. Rorvik, that "a wife can stroll through a special kind of market and make a selection from among one-day-old frozen embryos guaranteed free of all genetic defects and fully described as to sex, eye color, probable IQ, and so on. Following the purchase, the embryo can be thawed and then implanted under a doctor's supervision."[10]

Transplanting Animal Embryos

Dr. Hafez has also been experimenting with enormous multiples in cows and is convinced that the placenta holds the key. He believes that many women are not really sterile. If their placental functions could be aided, embryos that now shrivel unsuspected within them might have a chance at normal birth.

For Dr. Hafez, to produce mere "quints" with his cows would be failure. It is routine for him to achieve litters of a hundred. Not within one cow, of course!

He implants the embryos from a single cow into other hosts and achieves some incredible switch-abouts. A cow, like a woman, is born with many thousands of potential eggs in its ovaries but will ordinarily have no more than a dozen calves in its lifetime. Hafez can take anything from month-and-a-half-old calves to aging females, and by using two kinds of hormones (taken from pregnant mares and pregnant women) make his bovine patient produce huge quantities of ripe eggs.

He then fertilizes the eggs by artificial insemination and several days later flushes out these minute embryos. They can then be implanted, one or two to a cow, and arrive in due course at a normal birth. Born to an adopted mother, they are then genetically the offspring of a prize herd—"Rosie O'Grady" mothering "The Colonel's Lady" willy-nilly!

Such embryos can even be temporarily transplanted into the ovaries of rabbits for about fourteen days, during which time they are shipped to other continents to be reimplanted and brought to birth.

Sometime in the future, Hafez suggests, "women may have super embryos—the calculated combination of the best sperm *and* eggs— implanted in their wombs, selecting them from cold storage rather like packages of seed."

Sperm has already been kept viable in a freezer for more than a decade, and now Dr. Hafez reports that he has kept animal embryos for periods of up to twelve days, after which he has successfully thawed them out still alive.

By these fantastic means, he suggests, whole barnyards of animals and colonies of humans might be sent in test tubes to other planets to be nursed to maturity by expert biologists.

8 ESP AND PSYCHIC BONDS

Now we come to that disputed topic—ESP between multiples. Is there a psychic rapport between twins, particularly MZ twins? Mrs. Betsy Gehman, in her excellent book *Twins: Twice the Trouble, Twice the Fun,* assures us that her twins have no such gifts and that doctors she has questioned attribute these reports to the imaginations of adoring mothers.[1]

It is unfortunate for Mrs. Gehman and her readers that these physicians, skilled though they may be in their practice of medicine, are giving their personal opinions *as facts* in a discipline foreign to them. Actually a solid body of scientific research going back to Sir Francis Galton, the nineteenth-century father of the science of eugenics, supports the existence of psychic rapport between certain sets of identical twins. There are twins and twins. It is just as unrealistic to expect all twins to have extrasensory ability as to expect them all to have 20–20 vision or cast-iron digestive systems.

Sir Francis and more recent investigators have estimated that not more than one third of identicals have exceptional affinities, and it is among such pairs that we find the evidence for ESP communication. Psychological attitudes seem to promote or inhibit such empathy. Twins indifferent to each other are not likely to possess this subtle gift.

As a psychologist in the Los Angeles County Public School District, Mrs. Eloise Shields performed routine diagnostic work on pupils

referred to her for aggressive or withdrawn behavior, social malad-
justment, and similar problems. She used card-and-picture tests for
ESP and was asked during an interview if she found any difference
between withdrawn and aggressive children.

"Withdrawn children inhibit ESP from entering their unconscious,
or else they use it in a negative way to make the answer wrong
instead of right. The aggressive or outgoing children have some ESP
which they use in a 'pure' manner by giving correct answers beyond
what could be gotten by chance. Now, the children who manipulate
the people around them (their parents, brothers, sisters, teachers, and
other children) often have a stronger degree of ESP than other types
of personality. They may use it in either a negative or a positive
manner. If hostile to people, they use it negatively; if not hostile, they
use it in a positive way."

It seems likely that the percentage of identical twins who do influence or communicate with each other through supersensory channels
must have even more than a close, harmonious relationship. They
must also have some kind of mechanism in their dual psychological
and physical makeup—some interchange that permits this subtle
communication. Other conditons may be required that still remain to
be discovered. Meanwhile, now that parapsychology has become
"respectable" through its recent recognition by the American Association for the Advancement of Science, cooperation between the
various disciplines may bring about more complete understanding.

Coincidence or Psychic Influence?

Back in the 1870's when Sir Francis Galton was experimenting
with twins, he observed an example of duplicate gift-buying. He reported that identical twin A, "who happened to be in a small town in
Scotland, bought a set of champagne glasses which caught his attention as a surprise gift for his brother, B; while at the same time B,
being in England, bought a similar set of precisely the same pattern
as a surprise for A."[2]

One of our correspondents is Mrs. Laura Helser, who has traveled
the world with her husband, Lieutenant Colonel Loren E. Helser,
U.S.A.F. She and her sister, Elizabeth, are identical twins. At one
time when the Helsers were stationed in Ankara, Turkey, they
decided to celebrate Christmas using the traditional red and green

colors in their house decorations and gift wrapping. She wrote as follows:

> It was in October when I did our gift-shopping and got everything ready for mailing, due to the length of time it took for delivery from Turkey. I wrapped everything the same except the packages we were sending to Sis.
>
> For these I got some black paper and used Schiaparelli pink ribbon. When my husband asked me why I was using a different color scheme for her, I said I really didn't know, just wanted to, I guess. After Christmas Elizabeth wrote that my packages exactly matched the color scheme she had chosen to decorate the house for Christmas that year!

Coincidence or psychic influence? Who can say? But during earlier years the sisters did have ESP experiences. Her letter continues:

> When we were quite small, I was in the kitchen with Mother one day and suddenly said, "Hurry, Elizabeth has just fallen off Jack's bicycle and hurt her knee!" Without doubting, Mother followed, and I ran down the street because I knew just where she was. We found her still lying on the ground where she had fallen.

Mrs. Helser shared with Elizabeth the usual college capers—swapping dates and jobs and baffling sorority sisters. Although they lived on separate floors in the dormitory and the other girls watched like hawks to make certain there was no collusion, they came down to breakfast daily in identical clothing from shoes to dresses. Asked how it was done, they didn't know. It had never occurred to them that this was unusual. Never having heard of ESP, they felt like freaks. They were embarrassed by the stares and whispers when they were downtown shopping.

"We should hang signs on our backs saying, 'Yes, we are!' " they said. To this day they often say, "We need our signs."

But all this is explained as parallelism by the skeptical. Yet, while MZ twins may be split peas from the same pod with the same early environment, they are separate and distinct individuals making their way through life. There is a limit to which the theory of parallelism can be stretched.

Dr. Gerrit Jan S. Wilde, psychologist at Queen's University, Kingston, Ontario, Canada, is continuing there the twin research he began years before in Holland. At the University of Leyden and at Wilhelmina Hospital in Amsterdam he studied eighty-eight MZ and forty-two DZ pairs. Among the former twins were two brothers who married identical twin sisters. They shopped independently for the furnishings in their first homes.

Within a short time, says Dr. Wilde, the interiors of their homes "completely mirrored each other." Each Saturday they would buy flowers and without any discussion almost always chose the same blooms. Each couple's first child was born the same week, and the baby carriages they brought home from different stores were identical models.[3]

This is parallelism with a vengeance.

The Macrophage System

Some researchers hope to find a physical basis for all ESP cases. Among them is Dr. Hilda Gertrud Heine, a former lecturer at the University of New Zealand. In her book *The Vital Sense: The Implications and Explanation of the Sixth Sense,*[4] she gives lengthy data on the body's "chemical communication system," the macrophages. This organization of tiny amoeboid cells sends and receives impressions from below the threshold of normal perception.

She says that her book "represents an attempt to build a bridge between a very old field of inquiry and a very modern one: between clairvoyance and other occult phenomena on the one hand and communication research on the other."

Oversimplifying her explanation, this reticuloendothelial system consists of reticulin fibers (i.e., meshed, as in the network of a leaf) and of highly specialized cells known as macrophages. The latter may assume a number of forms, and like amoebas, they can change shape and have some freedom of movement. (For example, those under the skin surface can become detached during inflammation and migrate to the outer surface to collect and ingest poisonous material. They also secrete the fluid that lubricates body tissues.)

These cells, Dr. Heine suggests, are "the physiological and real part of the soul" and are the sense organ of the sixth sense—"a very elusive kind of sense organ."

In certain persons they are more sensitive than in others. They may also be stimulated by such factors as weather, the sea, pain, drugs, oxygen deprivation, change of pressure, rhythms, smells, etc. Then psychic awareness is briefly aroused—perhaps in both the transmitter and the receiver of the vision or impression.

In early childhood the activity of our macrophage system is most active and least inhibited. Thus young children are particularly apt to pick up the emanations and vibrations of others.

"Since the contact between twins is particularly close," she writes, "one would assume them to be knit by a very efficient telepathic communication system, and there is evidence to confirm this. The editors of *Phantasms of the Living* [a famous old casebook edited by Gurney, Myers, and Podmore in London in 1886] report four striking cases and give it as their opinion that the cases of telepathy among twins are more numerous than would be expected if the degree of relationship played no part."

We were struck by her statement that the macrophages, like all cells, need nourishment (especially with vitamins) and deteriorate if not properly supplied. May not this be the reason doctors are now finding that huge doses of vitamins are needed to combat retardation and mental illness?

With retardation, and differently with schizophrenia, the individual is much less aware or sensitive—so possibly the macrophages of his "communication system" are dulled.

These cells, Dr. Heine says, "act as our doctor and nurse." Closely tied to the nerve endings and fibers, they send information by various relays to other parts of our system. She believes that the sterile intellectual researcher receives information from the brain only, whereas the truly creative scientist has access to his macrophage relays.

But Dr. Heine herself does not seem to see beyond her own frame of reference. To explain all psychic phenomena, as she does, by the single answer—the bodily macrophage system—seems to us too limited and often far-fetched. That hers is one important explanation among others yet to be discovered appears more plausible.

Pain-Sharing between Twins

But what theory really explains such incidents as the following which testify to the curious sharing of pain among identicals?

Mrs. Joan Bryan, of East Rochester, Ohio, and her sister are the same twins who as children drew their parents' tickets in the church raffle. She wrote us that in October, 1956, she was living on Cape Cod in Massachusetts, while her twin, Joy, was in Olympia, Washington. Joy was suddenly stricken with a kidney infection and was taken to the Fort Lewis hospital by her husband. As he wheeled Joy through the hospital, Joan's husband was performing the same act at the Otis Air Force Base Hospital—the difference being that although Joan was suffering sharp pains, no cause for them could be found. After a series of negative tests, she was sent home with no medication and no explanation.

"We each have three children, two boys and one girl," Mrs. Bryan continues. "While I was in labor, we decided to try something we had heard during our studies of ESP. That was for her to try to take some of the pain from me. I was in labor all night but slept most of the time. Around eight the next morning the baby was born. The nurse who was with me all night was amazed. She said I had been having pains which I didn't even know I was having. This proved to me that Joy had accomplished what she was trying to do; besides I already had one child and knew the pains could have been a lot worse. When I talked to Joy later, she and my sister-in-law confirmed she was in quite a bit of pain and knew when I had Beth, because her pains stopped."

Dr. Ian Stevenson investigated a strong case of pain-sharing between adult twins. He interviewed a pair whom he called Mrs. Dora Martin and Mrs. Martha Morrison and quotes from a tape he made with them.[5]

Mrs. Martin and her husband, a physician, were traveling in Italy when she awakened with a severe pain in her chest and a strange fit of weeping. When he examined her, Dr. Martin estimated she might be coming down with something, though he saw no indication of sickness. But after a few hours in bed she felt fine. The pain she had described suggested a collapsed lung. Half-seriously her husband remarked that perhaps something was wrong with her pregnant sister, Martha, who had not written in a long time. She agreed it was possible.

When he interviewed her, Dr. Stevenson asked Mrs. Martin if she had ever experienced such pains before.

"No! It felt as if someone was taking the air out of my lungs."

Ten days after the incident she received a letter from her father.

Martha, in Wayne, Pennsylvania, had had a severe pregnancy and delivery. She had wakened with abnormal bleeding and was rushed to the hospital, but the baby presented an arm, and it was too late for a cesarean. She went into shock with great loss of blood and was unconscious for about four hours. When they all discussed this later, they realized it was about the same time on the other side of the Atlantic that Dora had awakened in pain—7 A.M.

When Martha came out of the anesthetic, they had a terrible time getting her to breathe and assumed it was due to her hard delivery. But blood clots had formed throughout her body, localizing in the lungs.

Describing her mysterious attack in Italy, Dora Martin said she had feared she was coming down with flu and that tears were pouring down her face, although she hadn't cried in ten years. Her husband corroborated that such anxiety was quite foreign to her. She said to Dr. Stevenson, "The only way I can describe it is to say it was as if someone put a black cloak over me."

Since the birth of her sister's child was premature, Dora had not been worried or expecting it. The dates coincided, but not the precise hours of the whole experience.

In assessing these pain-sharing cases it is essential to discover whether the twins are together or know what is happening, particularly if a deep feeling of sympathy can cause a responsive psychosomatic condition. But when they have no knowledge of each other's state and the sensations are nearly simultaneous, the explanation must involve extrasensory affinity.

In our files we have several cases of hospitalized children whose twins at home simultaneously experienced their pain. Serious heart surgery was involved in two instances. One was so interesting that we visited the mother and met her small triplets.

On March 21, 1960, Mrs. John Watson, of Torrance, California, became the mother of three boys—David, Daniel, and DeWayne. Much to her relief, they waited until after midnight, beginning at 12:03 A.M., and spaced themselves three minutes apart. She didn't want them born on different dates!

She knew she was having triplets four and a half months in advance. "No, I wasn't scared," she told us. "God made my body for this, so why should I be?"

But David came into the world with a rare heart malformation—

mitral stenosis—although it wasn't discovered at once because De-Wayne was the puny one. It took ten minutes for the doctor to get DeWayne breathing.

"Some doctors would give up after ten minutes," Mrs. Watson said, "but mine gave him a good swat and said, 'Dammit, we're going to win!' and he did."

The doctors waited until the triplets were three and a half years old before operating on David. Then he spent fifteen days in Harbor General Hospital and nine weeks recovering at home. While the surgery was in progress Daniel and DeWayne had to be given sedatives to overcome uncontrollable fright and coughing fits. Then, when the operation was over, they slept peacefully.

Psychosomatic Sympathy or ESP?

Can psychosomatic sympathy produce moles? A Louisiana couple, Lieutenant and Mrs. Burl Wolf, of Bossier City, had five-year-old twins who were so identical that when the girls entered school, their father went to the police for help in registering them. When detectives tried to match their footprints with those on their birth certificates, they found the prints just as confusing as the girls themselves. And since each of them insisted that she was the other, they were no help!

The Wolfs had assistance temporarily when a mole appeared on one child's forehead. But this didn't last, since soon one appeared on her sister's forehead. This was repeated at least three times. When one twin got a mole, it was only a matter of days or weeks until the other had one in approximately the same spot.[6]

Quite possibly this is psychosomatic, but it is not coincidence. As Ian Fleming's Goldfinger said, "Once is happenstance; twice is coincidence; three times is enemy action."

And how should the following incident be classified? Mrs. Vera Randall, of Chula Vista, California, had a ganglion develop on her wrist. Just before a surgical appointment to have it removed, her twin sister, Willie, and her husband drove down from Los Angeles. Although the visit was unexpected, Vera suddenly knew her sister was coming as she was washing the dishes. (A number of telepathic impressions seem to occur at the dishpan! Do they add weight to Dr. Heine's theory of the macrophages being stimulated by water?)

Vera was so certain that she sent her husband to the store for additional food. Fifteen minutes later they arrived.

It turned out that Willie also had a ganglion on her wrist and had gone to her doctor on the same day as Vera. Both identical twins were examined by Dr. Dale E. Hoyt, of National City, California, and at their request he signed the following statement:

Re: Vera Randall and Willie Hemphill. The above-named are a pair of identical twins. Each of these ladies has a ganglion on the distal end of the radius on her right hand. In each case the ganglion is approximately the same size, in exactly the same location, and has been noted for approximately the same duration.[7]

It should be noted that Vera and Willie had an unusual rapport. They had various illnesses at the same time, unaware of the other's affliction. This rules out psychosomatic sympathy. Willie, who had no children, suffered stomach pains on the three occasions when Vera was in labor.

"How could my sister have had sympathetic pains when she did not know I was in labor?" Vera asks.

The Mind versus the Brain

Just how closely is the mind anchored to the gray matter of the brain? Medical cases are on record in which the mind continues to function after large areas of the brain have been destroyed.[8]

In the classic nineteenth-century case of Phineas Gage, an explosion drove a thirteen-pound tamping bar completely through his skull. Although a large part of his brain and one eye were destroyed, Gage lived a normal life for years. Today the original bar and a cast of his skull are in the Harvard Medical Museum.

In 1953 a male infant, born in St. Vincent's Hospital, New York City, lived twenty-seven days without a brain but defied orthodox concepts of physiology by eating, crying, and reacting to stimuli. Doctors had no indication that the baby was in any way abnormal until an autopsy revealed that the cranial cavity contained only water!

Professor G. W. Surya reported the case of a man, insane for years, who suddenly became normal shortly before his death. "The autopsy revealed that there was practically nothing left in his brain pan." Thus his return to normalcy defies all medical explanations.

Professor Surya believed that the mind is the source of mental energy and the brain is comparable to a switchboard transmitting power and messages through the nervous system to the secondary neurocenters. When the switchboard is destroyed, emergency lines may be laid from mind to neurocenters, bypassing the brain. Thus full command of the faculties might be retained. Still other such cases are on record.

The electroencephalograph (EEG) is an instrument that records tiny electric currents in the brain on a graph. Not only do these patterns reveal that people can be grouped according to the types of their overall rhythms, but the patterns vary with passing thoughts. Anger, concentration, repose—each has its own typical pattern.

Through hypnosis the EEG shows up the distinction between the mind and the brain. H. Tudor Edmunds, Member of the Royal College of Surgeons in England, says that if the subject's eyes are closed but

he is made to *believe* they are open, his EEG still records that his eyes are closed. . . . If made to believe they are shut, the brain still records that his eyes are not only open, but seeing! So the *brain* is recording what is actually happening physically, while at the same time the *mind* is acting independently and completely believing the opposite.

. . . In this way it is found that deep sleep produced by a hypnotist causes little or no effect on the EEG rhythms, whereas normal sleep, or that produced by the action of an anesthetic . . . causes marked changes in the EEG findings . . . the mind can be deluded while the brain continues to function normally.

The subject of EEG and twins is discussed by another English expert, Dr. W. Grey Walter, in his book *The Living Brain.*[9] The alpha rhythms of identicals are very similar, but any developing changes in their characters are apt to show up in the other ryhthms. Alpha is the wave produced when the mind is very tranquil and (with rare exceptions) only with closed eyes. Beta waves show tension and frustration; theta, daydreaming and uncertainty; delta, infants' and sleeping adults' patterns.

But here again there are twins and twins.

In 1965 Doctors Thomas Duane and Thomas Behrendt, eye specialists at Jefferson Medical College in Philadelphia, made this discovery as an offshoot of an unrelated experiment—the photic-driving response to flashing lights. One person out of ten responds with a pattern of brain waves that match the light, but the nine remaining have their own frequency. The doctors advertised for identical twins, then changed the experiment to see how alike the brain waves were without the light.

The first pair of twins, who were medical students at the college, were seated in separate rooms eighteen feet apart with electrodes taped to their skulls. After repeated experiments the tapes were examined. Each time one brother closed his eyes, the alpha waves appeared on the tapes of both.

The doctors could hardly wait to find another set of twins, but when they did, the waves were not alike. Six or seven more sets of twins also failed to synchronize, then with twenty-three-year-old brothers, they got it again. To be sure that twinning was the factor, they matched each of the four twins with unrelated persons—and again, there was no correlation.

"The interesting thing," said Dr. Duane, "is that we aren't at all experts on ESP. We have done no work in this area. We have just this one very interesting finding which we want to get on the record."[10]

Dream Experiments with Twins

Perhaps the most fascinating use of the EEG is with dreams. Maimonides Medical Center in Brooklyn, New York, has a Dream Laboratory devoted to this work. Here Dr. Stanley Krippner has been engaged in controlled experiments in dream telepathy.

Some of his helper pairs are twins (both identical and fraternal). One remains awake to act as sender, or "agent," for the sleeping subject, or "receiver." The two are in separate, sound-deadened rooms with a one-way intercom. The EEG and a third person to monitor the brain waves of the sleeping subject are in still another room.

In dreamless sleep the eyes are quiet. But as soon as dreams begin, rapid eye movements (REM) show up on the graph. Then the technician buzzes the waking sender to look at his "target"—usually a colored picture—and try to send it telepathically to the dreamer.

The dreaming subjects are awakened at the conclusion of each REM period during the night, and their dream reports are recorded by them on tape. The purpose, of course, is to learn if the sleeper will pick up enough telepathic impressions to make the experiment "a hit." Both subjects and judges rank the hits and misses, and the hits are usually well above chance.

In another line of investigation, attempts were made to modify the procedures of Doctors Duane and Behrendt in Philadelphia. Instead of trying to induce alpha rhythms as these doctors had done, Maimonides researchers tried to block them. While one twin was producing alpha waves the other was given a light flash or had his hand dipped into ice water. Eight out of sixteen times the reaction of one twin showed some extrasensory perception of the ice-water hand-bath given the other.

Most of the work at the Dream Laboratory has concerned telepathy, but one study is being done on the dreams of pregnant women and another on those of transsexuals, both before and after their sex-change operation.

A number of dreams that seem to be in part prophetic were experienced. Dr. Krippner emphasizes that such dreams should not cause alarm:[11]

Dreams of the future, of other people's thoughts, and of distant events do seem to occur. We don't know why this happens or how this happens. Nevertheless, these events are apparently part of the life process—not a bizarre, abnormal peculiarity that should be feared or suppressed.

He continued with still wider implications:

It's my hunch that we'll eventually have to revise our image of man, on the basis of telepathic evidence. At present, psychology views each person as an alienated man, cut off from his surroundings . . . basically alone.

Telepathy may teach us that in the basic fabric of life everything and everyone is linked, that man is continuously enmeshed, that he is always an integral part of all life on the face of the earth.

Telepathic Messages between Twins

Our usual concept of telepathic messages is that they are occasional, crisis events—bringing knowledge of death, accident, or illness. Examples involving twins are the two following, from the monumental nineteenth-century *Phantasms of the Living*.[12]

The Reverend J. M. Wilson was headmaster of Clifton College, Cambridge. When he was a young man in his second term at Cambridge, he had a most peculiar experience. Although an athlete in excellent health, he was stricken one evening with a strange fit of trembling and weakness.

"I was frightened . . . totally unable to overcome it . . . resolving that I *would* go on with my mathematics, but it was in vain. I became convinced I was dying."

That afternoon a letter arrived announcing that his twin brother had died the evening before.

Although his brother had been ill for a long time, there was no reason to think his death was near. No feeling of his presence nor even a thought of him had accompanied his symptoms.

"I never experienced any similar nervous depression. It was a sort of panic fear, the chill of approaching death. The hours did not exactly coincide; my brother died some four hours before I was so seized." (Such delays are common with crisis telepathy.)

Case 77 follows in the same volume and concerns thirty-nine-year-old twin men-servants. James Carroll was a male nurse for an invalid in Wales while his twin was in Surrey. They had never been ill until Monday, June 17, 1878. James, in fact, was feeling very cheerful until near noon, when he was stricken with a mysterious depression. The brothers wrote at least twice a week, but his twin's last letter had been normal. The following Saturday James suffered another depression so severe that he fled in fright to the servants' quarters. Near collapse, he had just exclaimed, "My brother or I will break down," when a telegram arrived asking him to come. His brother was dangerously ill and died the following Monday.

His twin had become ill on the day James experienced his first odd depression, and at the time of the second, had been speaking of him in great distress. James secured statements from various persons substantiating the matter.

What parapsychologists call "crisis cases"—telepathy in times of danger, injury, or death—are remembered and recorded. But on subconscious levels there may be ESP rapport that is much more frequent and especially so between identical twins due to their fundamental affinity.

Dr. H. H. Price, Fellow of the British Academy and professor of logic at Oxford University, said in an address before the Society for Psychical Research in London that "the reason most of us appear to receive no telepathic impressions is that we may receive too many, so that no one of them makes any distinct or individual mark upon our minds.

"I will appeal to a frankly materialistic analogy, drawn from the more familiar world of the detective story," he continued. "When a certain object, say the poker, has been handled by a great number of people, it will be useless to look for thumbprints on it—not because there are none, but because there are too many, and they are all blended together into an undifferentiable mess."[13]

Thus identical twins who do possess this faculty may be able to identify chains of telepathic perception consciously, and there may be a steady subconscious flow of information, influence, or sensation. Perhaps this interplay can occur during sleep. We have one case in our files of young girl twins who woke up screaming. They had been experiencing the same nightmare of walking along the edge of a cliff and then falling.

Far more astonishing is a case reported by Professor H. H. Newman. While experimenting with identicals at the University of Chicago, he found a pair who when cramming for examinations, would divide their textbooks into two equal piles. Only one twin would study each pile, yet when the examinations were conducted, both twins seemed to have mysteriously absorbed the contents of all the books![14]

Dr. Robert A. Bradley, a prominent Denver obstetrician, frequently gives talks on ESP to young people.

"Hardly a talk goes by without interruption by squeals or recognition coming from the eager youngsters," he states.

> This is especially true when I illustrate the ability of identical twins to perceive each other's thoughts, aided perhaps not only by social and personal ties, but also by genetic bonds. An aware, thinking, alert grade-school teacher noticed that her young identical twin pupils took turns taking home books. On questioning them, she found her suspicions confirmed—they were taking turns studying, yet each passed the tests!
>
> Two handsome, sixteen-year-old twin boys in one group described how they did the same and bragged that the twin who didn't study got the best grades on exams!

A football coach in a local high school described how he could never scrimmage twin boys on opposite teams. No matter what play was called, the twin brother would know exactly where the ballplayer was going and tackle him immediately.[15]

When Dr. Joseph Banks Rhine was conducting his experiments in ESP at Duke University, he stated unequivocally that some twins were better at both sending and receiving than unrelated partners.

This was also found to be true by Doctors Carroll B. Nash and Dallas E. Buzby in tests conducted at St. Joseph's College, Philadelphia. Their report titled "Extrasensory Perception of Identical and Fraternal Twins" was published in the March–April, 1965, issue of the *Journal of Heredity*. Eleven pairs of identicals and fourteen pairs of fraternals—nine pairs of the latter being of the same sex—participated in the tests using Rhine's ESP cards.

"The two statistical indices used indicate greater similarity between the scores of members of identical twin pairs," the report stated. "The findings are consistent with the hypothesis that variations in ESP have a genetic basis. Methods were employed to preclude counterhypothesis to extrasensory perception as an explanation of the significance of the results."

Apparitions at the Time of Death

There are many stories of apparitions seen at the moment of death. This one, told by the well-known Washington newspaperwoman Ruth Montgomery, involves a twin.[16]

Loy Henderson, a former United States Ambassador to India, Iran, and Iraq, had an identical twin brother, Roy, with whom he had a very close bond. In their youth they were seldom separated, but when World War I broke out and both tried to enlist, the army rejected Loy.

So Roy Henderson was sent to Fort Riley while Loy went to Estonia for the Red Cross. Shortly afterward, Roy was released from service in order to have an infected kidney removed. He returned to Harvard while Loy stayed on after the armistice in command of a Red Cross unit dealing with Russian ex-prisoners. Sanitary conditions were terrible, and Loy became very ill. Lying in the hospital, he was overcome by the conviction that he was dying. Immediately a vision of Roy appeared by his bed. They talked of their grief at parting and said good-bye. Then Roy vanished.

But to his great surprise Loy recovered. Three days later he was taking a bath when his colonel called through the door that a cablegram for him had just arrived. Instinctively Loy knew that it bore word of his brother's death and stated that he didn't want to open it. The colonel, of course, declared this was nonsense and offered to read the message.

A stupefied silence followed. Sure enough, Henderson's twin brother, Roy, had died following infection from an extracted tooth at the same hour as Loy's farewell vision in the hospital!

9 THE ANOMALIES—SIAMESE TWINS AND ABNORMALITIES

When you come across a news item announcing the birth of another pair of Siamese twins, do you ever wonder what such a life must be like?

To most of us it is inconceivable—another person, a mirror-likeness of ourselves, bound to us by a band of living flesh. Suppose we were facing such a being—or as sometimes happens, bound back to back and unable even to see our alter ego without craning the neck or using a mirror.

Geneticists tell us that the time when the egg splits into two determines the formation of Siamese twins. If it splits soon after conception, all is well, and normal "identicals" are formed. But if splitting is delayed, probably beyond the tenth day after fertilization, Siamese or other abnormal births may result.

These twins share a single placenta, chorion, amnion, and navel cord. Such births are rare, perhaps 1 in 100,000, too uncommon for precise statistics. Although we know that the malformation occurs because of the late separation of the egg, the reason for this delay is not understood.

Such mistakes happen in all forms of life. Cats, for example, have been born with two heads and seven legs; calves and deer with two hind ends. There are also large two-headed trout, turtles, and snakes. Some hens lay double- or even triple-yolk eggs. Like identical twins, these phenomena are the product of a single ovum which splits, then forms two centers of organization close together. When these begin to

114

A Dutch artist's painting of quintuplets born in a farmhouse in Holland in 1719. History says that only two of these quints lived but that the bodies of the others were exhibited for some time to satisfy the crowds who came to gape at the "miracle." (Photo by the Bettmann Archive, Inc.)

Adapted from the Biddenden Maids' Easter cakes, stamped from boxwood dies made in 1814. These Siamese girls were born in Kent, England, in A.D. 1100 and died at age thirty-four. Their dress is of a much later era.

Thirteenth-century triplets in swaddling clothes with their nurses. From ancient times into the seventeenth century, babies at birth were bathed, salted all over, then tightly bound, including their heads. The bandages prevented the slightest movement and were usually removed only once a day! This continued for several months. About half of the tiny victims died.

The "Twin Brothers," adapted from carnival handbills in London, about 1716. The third hand is disputed. The half-brother to the left had good sight, speech, and appetite but felt no motion below the point of juncture at the side. (*Drawn by Alta Happ*)

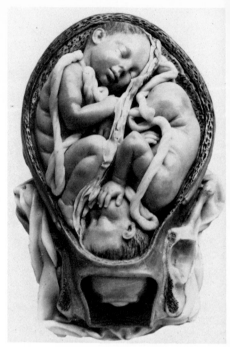

Wax model of a pregnant uterus containing dichorial (fraternal) twins, opened anteriorly. Sculptor, G. B. Manfredini. (*Reproduced from Twins in History and Science by courtesy of Professor Luigi Gedda and Charles C. Thomas, Publisher*)

Istituto Gregorio Mendel (The Twin Institute), Rome, Italy. (*Photo courtesy of the institute's director, Professor Luigi Gedda*)

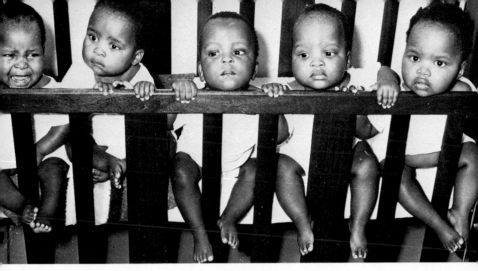

The Tukutese Quintuplets. Left to right: Tandeka, Zoleka (girls), and Tandekile (also known as Mbambile), Tembekile, and Kululekile (boys). Taken just before their first birthday at their home in Mdantsane, near East London, South Africa. Born February 6, 1966, their total weight was twenty-three pounds eight ounces, more than ten pounds heavier than the Dionnes and probably a world record. Delivery took one hour seven minutes. (*Photo by Roger Wakefield, Johannesburg, South Africa*)

A basketful of twins born within nine months and twenty-three days to Mr. and Mrs. Luther Davidson, of Columbus, Ohio. Pat (left) and Patricia (right) arrived January 26, 1960. Keith and Brad (center) followed on November 18, 1960. The Davidsons, who had longed for a playmate for their twelve-year-old Linda, were overwhelmed. (*Photo by UPI*)

American farmer from Putnam County, New York, surrounded by his five pairs of twins. (*Photo by the Bettmann Archive, Inc.*)

Twins Tatiana and Marina Givotsky, of Closter, New Jersey. At two years, Marina dials the phone. Tati assumes passive role of waiting for the sound. The twins are the oldest of four children. (*Photo by Susan Szasz*)

Fumbling but determined, Marina puzzles over Tati's strap as she seeks to correct a problem of drooping overalls. The daughters of an artist, both girls have been encouraged in creative directions. (*Photo by Susan Szasz*)

Can this possibly be mere coincidence? These "astrological twins"—unrelated little girls—were born in the same hospital in White Plains, New York, within five minutes of each other on February 20, 1947. They are Jean Henderson and Joyce Ritter (or vice versa!). (*Photo by C. Bernstein from Black Star*)

Though you wouldn't know it from this photo, Gary and Lary Hutchens were born Siamese twins, linked at the spine by nerve fiber and common spinal canal. They were surgically separated seventeen days after birth in a ninety-minute operation. (*Photo by Wide World*)

Separated Siamese twins, Giuseppina and Santina Foglia, of Asti, Italy, with their mother. (*Photo by UPI*)

Johnny Eck (Eckhardt) standing on his hand. Taken on the
M-G-M lot in 1932 for the film "Freaks," this is Johnny's
favorite photo. (*Courtesy of Johnny Eckhardt*)

Johnny with his brother Robert Eckhardt,
at the Cleveland, Ohio, Great Lakes
Exposition in 1937. (*Courtesy of Johnny
Eckhardt*)

Famous twins and rival advice columnists Ann Landers (top) and Dear Abby (bottom). Ann
has a famous collection of stuffed and sculpted owls; Abby leans to monkeys.

Twincerely Yours—The Rowe Twins, LaVona ("Lala 2") and LaVelda ("Lala 1"). International Twins Association officers, dancers, models, photographers. (*Photo by Chicago Daily News*)

The Tremblays, of St. George, Quebec: Francine, Raymonde (her twin died in infancy), Ronaldo Françoise, Ronad, Julien, Clement, Jules, Christien, Christiane, Jacqueline (concealed), Jacques, and their beaming parents. (*Photo by John Vachon*)

Twin-getherness—identical twins marry identicals and share a single home in Thornton, Colorado. In a double wedding in 1954 Herbert and Delbert Chase married Jean and Jane Sweet. They are seated here with Herbert's son Maurice and wife, Jean, on the left. Delbert is on the far right with Jane and their daughter Emmajean. (*Photo by UPI*)

Triplets in cap and gown. Paulette, Annette, and Suzette Yeats (from left) of
Sierra Madre, California, receiving their degrees from Pasadena City College.
(*Photo by the Los Angeles Times*)

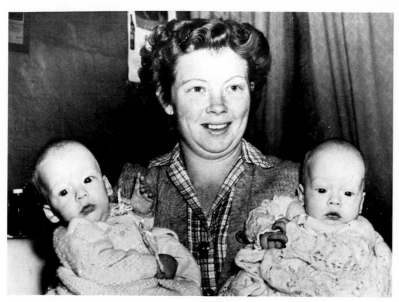

World's record twins—born fifty-six days apart in different years in King George V Memorial
Hospital in Sydney, Australia. Their mother, Mrs. A. Goodwin, of Newton, Sydney, beams
proudly. Denis, born December 16, 1952, weighed 3 pounds 10¾ ounces, and David, born
February 10, 1953, weighed 5 pounds 9 ounces. The Associated Press states: "They are
authentic twins and the British Medical Association report says the interval between the births
is a world record." (*Photo by Wide World*)

Celebrating their ninety-eighth birthday together on February 10, 1964, the Duckworth twins, of Fillmore, California, were considered to be the oldest twins in the United States. Mattie, left, holds Sarah's hand. (*Photo by UPI*)

Seeing triple on seventy-fifth birthdays in Cleveland, Ohio. From the left, Mrs. Ida Ellis, Mrs. Ruth DeMoss, and Mrs. Lee Farmer. The triplets were born on a farm near Bowling Green, Kentucky, and kept warm in shoe boxes near a potbellied stove. All three are widows. (*Photo by UPI*)

Mothers of Twins Club Christmas party in Escondido, California. (*Photo by Mary Thomas Peterson*)

Puppies from the same litter born thirty days apart near Hamilton, Michigan. Mrs. Roland Frank holds a pup twice the size of the one held by her husband. The mother dog, Toto, gave birth to the big puppy on April 3, 1970, but waited thirty days to deliver four more. Since the normal period of pregnancy for dogs is sixty-two days, this would be similar to some four months apart for human multiples. (*Photo by the Prosch-Jensens, Fennville, Michigan*)

expand and differentiate, instead of dividing again properly, they fuse.

The Biddenden Maids

One of the earliest recorded cases of Siamese twins dates back to the twelfth century. In the year 1100 the "Biddenden Maids" were born in the hamlet of that name in the county of Kent, England. The parents of Mary and Eliza Chulkhurst were in comfortable circumstances, and because the girls were heiresses in a modest way, their memory was preserved for centuries.

Mary and Eliza bequeathed twenty acres of land to the church wardens of the parish and their successors. The rental from this land was to be used in perpetuity for an Easter remembrance. Cakes bearing the image of the girls were to be distributed to all strangers, with bread and cheese given to the poor of the parish.

Eight hundred years later this ceremony was still carried out, and the property was known as the Bread and Cheese Lands. In 1896 the rental came to about $155 yearly, which at that time paid for about 300 cakes (merely flour and water) and 540 quartern loaves with 470 pounds of cheese! Originally the distribution had been made in church, but this became too noisy.

A picture of the boxwood dies cut for the cakes in 1814 is reproduced in this book. This shows the Maids joined at both the hips and shoulders—a malformation not known to have occurred since, and it was probably the artist's error. It may have arisen from their habit of walking with their arms about each other's necks, simplified in the drawing into fusion.

Mary and Eliza lived to be thirty-four years old. Which of them died first the church records do not show, but the other refused the offer of surgeons to operate. When one recalls that the twelfth-century surgeon, or chirurgeon, was merely a barber and that the only anesthetic was a stiff slug of whiskey, it is easy to understand why death seemed preferable. Said the surviving twin, "As we came together, so we will also go together," which she did within six hours.

Parasitic Terata

In fifteenth-century Scotland another pair, of a type known to doctors as *parasitic terata,* lived at the court of James III. These

"Scottish Brothers" had only two lower limbs between them, so that learning to walk must have been a grave problem, overbalanced as they were by a dual body from the waist up. Probably they used some type of crutch.[1]

But they were such a tremendous attraction in that isolated and primitive court that the king went to great pains to have them taught music, languages, and courtly accomplishments. No doubt this bizarre pair standing on the rush-strewn floor of the bleak stone dining hall, strumming lutes as they sang a ballad, made a striking novelty. As he watched them with his nobles from his dais, the king must have bragged a bit about his twins, whose fame was spread by travelers clear to Rome.

Holding strong and often conflicting opinions, these brothers frequently came to blows, beating each other with their four arms. It was told as a marvel that neither of them could feel the other's sensations above the waist.

Some time after the murder of their royal patron in 1488, the end came to the brothers in their twenty-eighth year with the death of one of them. For five days, as an old manuscript put it, the other "moaned piteously as he crept about the castle gardens, carrying with him the dead body of the brother from whom only death could separate him and to whom death would again join him."

In those days such strange anomalies were sure of an easy life if they found a noble patron. In order to shine socially it was almost necessary for the higher nobility to have at least a dwarf as an entertainer, and twin dwarfs were a king's prize. These court "fools" were far from foolish and could get away with impertinences that would cost normal men their heads. Catherine de' Medici kept three sets of twin dwarfs, and a king in old Denmark valued his dwarf so highly that he made him prime minister.

Nearly 330 years after the time of the Scottish Brothers an old English carnival handbill shows another pair as they appeared in 1715 at a London sideshow.

"The Twin Brothers" were not complete Siamese, for the "half man" was attached at the right side of a body that was otherwise stalwart and well formed. They had only two arms between them. Both ate and drank with gusto, and they, too, had separate sensations in the upper trunk only.

The Strange Case of Edward Mordake

A "weird and melancholy story" from the records of an early day tells of Edward Mordake, heir to one of the noblest peerages of England, who because of his terrible deformity would not even see members of his family. His face was handsome, but on the back of his head was another masklike face, a girl's, "lovely as a dream, hideous as a devil." While he wept at his misfortune his "Devil Twin" would smile and sneer like a schizoid personality.

He declared that it whispered to him all night, and though no one else could hear an audible voice, the lips did move constantly. Mordake was a scholar and a fine musician, but in time his affliction overpowered his reason. He begged his doctors, Manvers and Treadwell, to remove the devil-twin, and when they insisted it was impossible, he somehow obtained poison and killed himself. How much of this melodrama is true no one can say today.

Other pairs recorded are the Hungarian Sisters (1701–1723) and the Sardinian Twins, Ritta and Christina, born in Sassari, Sardinia, in 1828. The Hungarian Sisters traveled with carnivals in Germany, Holland, Italy, Poland, and England. At nine years of age they were sent to a convent, where they died at twenty-two. During their travels they were examined by many famous doctors and naturalists. They were joined back to back, fused at the pelvis, with only two legs.

The parents of the Sardinians were very poor, and this was the mother's ninth confinement. These unfortunate children died of cold when their impoverished parents took them to Paris for exhibition, only to have authorities forbid it because pregnant women might be "marked" by the sight. A postmortem revealed that a single pericardium enclosed both hearts, but the digestive organs and even the uterus were double. The small skeleton is still preserved in Paris.

The Two-Headed Nightingale

A far more attractive and remarkable pair of little Negro girls won worldwide fame in the nineteenth century as singers. Their stage billing as "The Two-Headed Nightingale" was quite unjust, for they were a well-formed pygopagus—that is, joined at the buttocks. These little girls, Christine and Millie—born to slaves on a Columbus

County, North Carolina, plantation on July 11, 1851—also were the ninth confinement of their mother. As usual, her other children were normal.

When they were only four years old, they appeared as singers at the Egyptian Hall in London. Also called "The African Twins," they entertained with plantation songs. Millie, a contralto, was weaker physically but had the stronger will and dominated Christine, a soprano.

An old poster shows two cute little girls in low-necked, ruffled dresses with full skirts. They responded so well to education that at twenty-two they spoke several languages and were well known as singers and guitarists. No information is given as to their later fate except that they survived for some years after in show business.

Chang and Eng

The most famous of these twins were the original Siamese, Chang and Eng (meaning "left" and "right"). Today conjoined twins are termed Siamese just because these famous brothers were discovered in Siam. Though actually of Chinese parentage, they were born in Bangesu, Siam, on April 15, 1811.

The boys were great athletes, swimming, diving, and climbing like the rest of their mother's brood, in which were several sets of normal twins. The band of flesh joining them from breastbone to abdomen— about three and a half inches long and some eight inches around— was very flexible and permitted them to stand or lie down back to back. When resting, they found it more comfortable to put their arms around each other's shoulders.

At this late date it is hard to separate fact from fancy, since showman P. T. Barnum embroidered their story to circus propor- tions. One tale says that a British merchant found them at thirteen, just as King Chowpohyi had ordered them put to death as a bad omen, and bought them. Another version says an American sea cap- tain sensed their great potential as a profitable enterprise in show business and shanghaied them. At any rate they escaped from Siam.

In Boston they became an immediate sensation. After Harvard doctors examined them in 1829 they sailed for London. They were shown to 300,000 people over a 2,500-mile circuit in England alone. In London, the Royal College of Surgeons had them to tea, and a romantic young lady named Sophia fell madly in love with them, causing such a furor of legal arguments in the press about bigamy that the boys fled the country. When their manager made off with the funds, the twins went back to New York on their own and found Barnum eager to employ them.

The twins stayed with Barnum five years, saving sixty thousand dollars, and then started out on their own. Touring North Carolina in the 1840's, they were so delighted by the simple hill people that they bought a large farm and settled there. Soon they were in great demand at house-raisings, for in spite of their small size they could, unaided, lift a house-framing at the corner.

Romance budded again, possibly with the help of the sixty thousand dollars, and at twenty-eight they married the daughters of a farmer named Yates. Chang married Adelaide and Eng, Sarah Ann. But the birds in their little nests did not agree. Neither wife liked the other female in the macabre union. Finally they solved this by separate homes, three miles apart where, in turnabout fashion, each twin spent three days as unquestioned lord of that particular manor.

Naturally they were the subjects of both ribald and legal conjectures. Lawyers delighted in quibbling as to the penalty if one committed a crime or signed contracts separately. It was finally decided that they could act either jointly or separately in all matters of property but must marry individually and their offspring inherit separately.

They had twenty-two children: Eng fathered seven boys and five girls; Chang, seven girls and three boys. All were intelligent and of normal size, but two of Chang's were deaf-mutes. Several became bankers and army officers. One was a president of the Union Pacific Railway.

Though many visitors tried, it was impossible to discuss separate topics with them, for each would finish the other's sentences and claim to know the other's thoughts. They sometimes opposed each other in politics and enjoyed chess and checkers, but they never played together. What fun would that be when each foresaw the other's play?

They longed to be separated and visited a new physician after each tour, but no doctor would operate.

In 1873, returning from Europe, Chang suffered a stroke. After recovery he became moody and deaf—but only in the ear next to Eng! Irascible Chang made life difficult. When drunk, he would break and burn furniture while Eng followed him helplessly through his frenzies. In retaliation Eng delighted to torment sleepy Chang by sitting up all night playing checkers. As Chang drooped in stuporous anger, their wives fomented new quarrels. But through all of Chang's bouts with alcohol, Eng remained a teetotaler.

It was Chang's willfulness that led to their death, for he caught a severe cold at his and Adelaide's house. Against Eng's protest, at the end of the three days Chang insisted on keeping to their long-established routine. Through a sleety drizzle they set off for Eng's house in their open carriage.

Chang grew rapidly worse. One Friday evening in January, 1874, he got up in the wee hours, complaining that lying in bed caused pains in his chest. They sat quarreling by the fire in their specially built chair until Eng finally got his partner back to bed. When Eng woke, Chang was cold in death.

"My last hour has come!" he cried in panic.

The distraught family summoned their physician to perform the operation that would sever the dead from the living. But before he could get there Eng was seized with such convulsions of fright that he was dead within two hours, although his health had been fine.

The College of Physicians in Philadelphia performed the autopsy. Chang had died of a cerebral clot, but they found nothing wrong with Eng. The examination suggested, however, that no operation performed with the medical knowledge available at that time could have safely divided them.

The twins left behind a few relics that the family still treasures—their special chair, a double-length gold watch chain used by them both, and a somewhat mysterious bundle of ancient Siamese script, beautifully written on bits of parchment. If taken to scholars for translation, what fascinating tale would unfold?

A number of other Siamese twins have appeared in show business, but Nate Engle, of Ringling Brothers and Barnum & Bailey's Combined Shows, said he doubted that any real ones are on exhibit today.[2] The act is easily faked and successful surgical operation has grown too common for the condition to be tolerated needlessly. However, Siamese who share a vital organ will rarely survive to maturity.

Vaudeville Duos

A male pair, the Filipino Twins, was well known in vaudeville. Simplico and Lucio Godina performed with their wives, who were also one-egg twins although not Siamese. Professor Newman studied these twins and found them quite dissimilar in height and the shape of their heads. The Godinas were very active physically, dancing and roller-skating as part of their act. When Lucio, the smaller, caught cold and died of pneumonia, they were promptly separated surgically, but a few days later Simplico succumbed to an infection of the nervous system.

Another vaudeville pair, Rosa and Josepha Blazek, was born January 20, 1878, in Skerychov, Bohemia. Their publicity photographs show them joined in the pelvic region. One of the girls could sleep while the other was wide awake, and they delighted to eat at different times and demand different foods. One relished salads, the other detested them, and they were stubborn opponents when it came to beer and wine.

In 1900 Rosa gave birth to a baby boy in a hospital in Prague. But someone—possibly her showman brother for publicity purposes—started the rumor that it was Josepha who had been seduced! The child's father was willing to marry either or both girls, but the church and lawyers forbade the wedding. Although Josepha had only a rudimentary vagina and uterus and did not feel Rosa's labor pains, she did feel the discomfort of the final birth, since the sisters had only one vulva. Josepha's breasts also held milk, but she continued to menstruate until eight weeks before the child was born.

The Blazeks were still active in vaudeville when in 1922 Josepha was hospitalized with jaundice in Chicago. Rosa had only a hint of the disease, but Josepha's condition was so grave that the doctor advised a separation. But their brother-manager refused. Who was to pay for such an operation when their earning power would cease? Let them die! So on March 30, 1922, Josepha died of jaundice, and Rosa, of course, followed in less than two days—a grim spectacle for even hospital attendants to watch.

Siamese versus Normal Identicals

The question of childbearing with female Siamese twins is interesting. In his enormous computerized files on twins Professor Luigi Gedda, the famous Roman geneticist, has other cases of such pregnancies where only one twin felt the pain, but both were able to nurse the baby. Dr. Alan Guttmacher, who studied a pair of conjoined twins, also found that when one gave birth, both were able to suckle the child.

Although one would naturally expect Siamese to be more alike than ordinary one-egg twins, this is not the case. Newman said that "almost without exception they were more different in various ways than any but a very few pairs of separate one-egg twins." He related that Keeler found mirror-imaging common; comparing a rather large number of stillborn Siamese with ordinary one-egg twins, 73 percent had this characteristic. Gedda and Lionel S. Penrose, a well-known geneticist with the Galton Laboratory, University College in London, also report both physical and mental differences more marked than with ordinary identicals.

When Newman examined the female Hilton Siamese twins he found them attractive but less similar than almost any separate one-egg twins he knew. One was nearly two inches taller, and they showed great differences in temperament and ability.

Born in 1908, they were abandoned by their parents and taken into a carnival. These twins aroused quite a storm when they were refused marriage licenses in both New York and Chicago. Such an event, said both courts, would create a complicated moral problem and could not be allowed. Vaudeville receipts naturally soared.

At twenty-three Daisy and Violet had had enough. In a sensational court hearing in San Antonio, Texas, they charged that their promoter had held them in bondage. They said their "slavery" had grossed him two million dollars. The court freed them from his control, and they then became a vaudeville team, the Hilton Sisters Revue.

In 1936 Daisy married, and five years later her sister married a dancer, but both marriages ended in divorce. In 1962 they arrived in Charlotte, North Carolina, for a stage appearance, and when their money ran out, they found a steady job weighing produce at a supermarket. On January 4, 1969, friends found them dead of the flu at age sixty in their little home.

Surgical Separation of Siamese Twins

Conjoined twins have, of course, been a challenge to doctors for centuries. As early as A.D. 945 a pair was exhibited in Rome but was rushed out of the city by the authorities in superstitious fear. When one died, the doctors separated them, but the other died, too. He is said to have survived three days, which is remarkable enough in those primitive times. Such an operation did succeed in late seventeenth-century Switzerland, when doctors separated a pair "united belly to belly" by tissue and cartilage only. Throughout history others have been separated experimentally after death, and the facts recorded.

The operation on the Brodie twins in the 1950's lasted almost thirteen hours. The boys were joined at the head, which is less common, and Rodney Dee was able to survive his brother, Roger, because he retained a vein needed for drainage of the brain. At first, he led a nearly normal life, but a leakage in his brain caused his condition to deteriorate. On May 28, 1963, he choked on a mouthful of food his father was feeding him and died within moments, aged only eleven.

Among recent Siamese twins are two little Italian girls, Guiseppina and Santina Foglia. Conjoined at the base of the spine by a bony formation, they were delicate from birth. The surgery that would separate them was hazardous.

In May, 1965, a team of twenty-four specialists crowded an operating theater to watch the attempt to effect a surgical separation of the twins. New equipment, including a special table that could be divided after surgery, had been imported. As the four-inch strip of flesh between the two girls was severed, the blood vessels they shared were clamped. Then two teams of surgeons rebuilt the tissue and gave each little girl a piece of artificial intestine.[3]

When for the first time in their brief lives the twins woke in separate beds, little Guiseppina reached out her arms to her sister. "You're so far away!" she cried in alarm. And then looking down at her own body, "Is it really me? Am I truly myself?"

Six years later the twelve-year-olds were happily riding bikes to the village school in Asti, Italy. Their mother says their years of being bound together have left no emotional scars, and physicians have assured her that they will be able to marry and bear children.

Today surgeons are making vast strides in severing Siamese twins successfully, even when the liver is involved.

About a century and a half after Chang and Eng gave the name of "Siamese" to conjoined twins, two beautiful little girls were born in Siam. Like Chang and Eng, they had a common liver. Surrendered by impoverished parents to the care of the Women's and Children's

Hospital in Bangkok, they were discovered there in 1953 by an American hospital volunteer, Florence Atkinson.[4] Her husband was on a tour of duty with an American governmental agency. These seven-month-old mites—doomed, attendants said, to die—tugged at her heart with their enormous dark eyes and enchanting smiles.

The Buddhist doctor insisted they would bleed to death in an operation. Their religion also forbade it: Risking a life was a sin, interference with karma, or fate. Heartsick, Florence and another American woman, Mrs. Frances Sessions, determined somehow to save the tiny twins.

The Atkinsons were friends of Dr. Lester B. Dragstedt, chief surgeon at Billings Memorial Hospital at the University of Chicago. He wrote about a new technique for severing a liver, using a gelatinous blood coagulator called gelfoam. Provided little Napit and Prissana had normal gallbladder connections and separate bile ducts, there was a chance he could save the twins. He offered to waive his surgical fee.

But air fares alone would cost over four thousand dollars! The twins could die before a fund was set up, and the Buddhist doctor would refuse on religious grounds, even though X rays were reassuring. How could they raise such a sum quickly and practically shanghai the twins?

And suppose the children died in Chicago? Public anger might flare, injuring the work the United States was doing in Thailand. But the Prime Minister's wife, Lady La-iad, promised that if they could raise the money, she would help.

"Now all we need is money!"

Florence's words were lighter than her hopes, but once more events lined up in her favor. Harold E. Stassen arrived as director of the Foreign Operations Administration and cut through the red tape.

So the twins, now nearly two years old, were flown to Chicago with the head nurse, Jirapon Karsemsak. On March 29, 1955, the operation was successfully performed. The twins' exceptionally large liver helped, for liver tissue can regenerate, and each half would grow again—providing the surgeon could forestall their bleeding to death.

Throughout the three-and-a-half-hour operation, large quantities of gelfoam were sprayed on constantly. More than once, as Dr. Dragstedt had to pause for the coagulant to take hold, the staff feared for the children's life. Then it was over, and the little girls were put into the same bed to avoid any emotional shock when they came out of the anesthetic.

Exactly two months after they had left Thailand, Nurse Jirapon brought them home. But as wards of the state they had to return to the hospital. The Atkinsons were eager to adopt them, and the Siamese doctor agreed. He asked only that they wait till August 17, the day chosen by the state astrologers as best for the children.

But by March, months after the twins had become part of their family, the adoption papers had mysteriously not come, though the Atkinsons were scheduled to leave for home in the spring. General Prayune, Minister of Public Health, explained the problem. The Communist Member of Parliament from the province where the twins were born claimed the adoption was a United States plot to exploit the children!

"Have *you* ever spent a penny to help these children?" the general demanded of him. "Do *you* want them?"

The general won, but by law, wards of the state could not be readopted. However, the state could give them back to the parents, who could sign them over to the Atkinsons.

Florence was close to tears. "What if they won't!"

She endured a week of frantic anxiety, but with another baby on the way the parents signed the papers willingly.

And on February 23, 1961, the family appeared before Federal Judge John O. Henderson in Buffalo, New York. Starry-eyed and pigtailed, the twins swore allegiance to the flag and took the oath. As he shook hands with them afterward, the judge smiled broadly.

"You're the cutest kids I've ever naturalized," he told them.

Prissana looked up at him soberly. "You know, a long time ago we used to be Siamese twins!"

The judge looked at their mother, smiling again. "But not anymore. You're American twins now, for life!"

Even more extraordinary and unfortunate than regular Siamese are a pair of Russian girls, Masha and Dasha, who like the Scottish Brothers in the fifteenth-century court, have only one leg apiece, plus a third vestigial one. They were born on January 4, 1950, and from infancy have been reared in Moscow clinics, where they were given many tests.[5] Since each girl controls one leg, special exercises were necessary to teach them to coordinate. They could not walk at all until the age of five. But now through practice they can even dance, ride a bicycle, and climb ladders.

Professor Pyotr Anokhin, of Moscow's Institute of Prosthetics, who has supervised them from birth, says they are very different in personality: Masha is "a light-minded chatterbox who already flirts with boys," and Dasha, the dominant twin, is serious, quick, and studious. It was she who thwarted the doctors' plans to remove the useless and hampering extra leg by becoming hysterical. Each can feel pain only in her own half of their conjoined bodies.

The girls' pelvic bones are linked, and their spines connect at the coccyx. The spinal cords themselves, of course, are separate, hence so are their sense reactions. Since the circulatory system is interconnected, any intravenous injection spreads rapidly, but they can become ill separately. They have a single reproductive and urinary system and one bladder, but four kidneys, which means that they do not always wish to urinate at the same time.

To most of us these cases seem incredibly sad and life in a sideshow downright horrible. Yet, actually, carnival life seems to be far happier for these children than as the weird members of a normal family and the butt of countless cruelties.

In a fascinating article, "A Rare Look at Rare People," Daniel P. Mannix tells of a "Pig-Faced Boy" who had the respect due a great star.[6] "He was extremely proud of his appearance" and sneered at those who faked deformity with adhesives. " '*They* are just ordinary people, you know, but I really look like a pig,' he told me," said Mannix, "and he said it proudly." A family of pinheads, when separated from the carnival and institutionalized by well-meaning people, were wretchedly unhappy. "Perhaps the reason we feel an obligation to dislike freaks today," Mannix suggests, "is our current passion for uniformity."

Doctors frequently haunt the sideshows and learn as much from living "freaks" as from autopsies. The Alligator and Rubber Skinned Men and the Three-Legged Women give new insights into the nervous, muscular, and venous systems.

All these complicated and confusing factors should be a comfort to mothers who grieve over miscarriages. Often it is nature's kindness, eliminating malformed babies. According to a study at the University of Rochester, New York, chromosome abnormalities were found in tissue cultures from twenty-four out of fifty-four such fetuses. Since this is always associated with severe deformities and mental aberrations—and perhaps also with criminal and violent types—it would seem that the spontaneous expulsion of these fetuses in early pregnancy is really a blessing instead of a tragedy.

Teratomas—Dormant Twins

Still rarer than these circumstances, fortunately, are the occasions when a twin lies dormant within a body for many years, undiscovered, and then has to be surgically removed.

These growths are called *teratomas* and in ancient times were prized for divination. Among priests and seers the various abnormalities in their formation had special interpretations. Such secret meanings usually applied to the kingdom itself or to the person of the ruler, although at times they were interpreted as relating to the parents. At least some authorities speculate that teratomas are twins; others consider them tumors derived from the germ cells.

In one modern case of a teratoma an American woman was thought to have developed a tumor after her children were born. But when it was removed, it proved (if the above speculation is correct) to be not a tumor or a fetus but her twin. It had somehow lain quiescent within her abdomen for many years. Apparently the birth of her last child stimulated it, and it had become malignant. Peritonitis set in, but after some critical days she recovered. Her chart is reproduced on page 151 with the permission of *Dell's Horoscope* magazine.

These strange cases have been known throughout history and some of them are well authenticated. They happen even to children, and to men as well as women. Termed *fetus in fetu,* they might be described (incorrectly, of course) as cases where a man or child is pregnant with his own brother or sister!

Two recent cases are interesting. On January 31, 1953, in a Fort Wayne, Indiana, hospital, a Siamese-twin-like growth was removed from the back of an Ohio dairy farmer, then sixty-one years old. This "included twin" was found to be enclosed in a sac, about five and a half inches long and one and a half inches in diameter. Entirely concealed within the spinal canal in the small of his back, it had so choked off the nerve impulses that the patient had always had spindly legs.

A Reuters news dispatch, dated February 21, 1953, tells of "The

Man Who Had a Baby." A teen-aged railroad worker named Yoshinobu Nakan, of Osaka, Japan, complained of pains in his chest.
Suspecting a lung ailment, the doctors operated. Embedded in his
lung they found a *growing* baby girl. The embryo was the size of a fist
and perfectly healthy. The dispatch summarized the finding as
follows:

> Chief surgeon Masatoshi Naito explained that the embryo was a
> malformed twin development at birth. Yoshinobu should have had
> a twin sister but the twin egg was absorbed into his body early in his
> mother's pregnancy. It remained dormant there for years. Then, as he
> reached puberty, the change in hormone equilibrium in his body caused
> the embryo to grow again.

The "twin" was successfully removed, and the dispatch reported
that Yoshinobu was recovering.

As we were gathering this data we learned that a friend, as well as
her sister, had each had such "twins." Our friend's "twin" was not
discovered until after her third operation for ovarian cysts, when the
surgeon found she had a teratoma also. It was about the size of a
grapefruit—a mass of tissue, bone, and hair. Her doctor was amazed
to find that she (although not her sister) also had a third normal
kidney. Whether this oddity stemmed from the same cause as the
teratoma he could not say. He told them that such growths occurred
when the tendency to twinning was dwindling off in the family line,
but our geneticist consultant says this idea is pure speculation.

Teratomas (which when cystic are also called dermoid cysts) may
occur anywhere in the body, quite remote from the uterus, and
usually are not attached to any organ. On rare occasions they have
been fastened to some body part by a cord suggestive of the umbilical
cord.

It would seem, then, that when a history of twinning exists in a
family, if a woman develops ovarian cysts, the possibility of an
accompanying fetal cyst should be investigated.

One can well imagine that such occurrences, startling enough
today, might in more superstitious times be construed to foretell
disaster.

10 HOW IT FEELS TO BE A TWIN

"Being a twin, there's no such thing as loneliness. I have someone I can trust completely."

"Having a twin is fun. There's a lot of social pleasure in being alike. If I weren't a twin, I would not have been the center of attention in school and on the street."

"When one of us has a problem, it's a problem for both of us. We solve it together."

These were some of the replies given Dr. Robert Sommer, psychologist at the University of Alberta, Canada, in response to questions put to twins concerning their emotional reaction to twinship. More than half of the identicals he studied told him that at some time in their lives they had experienced moments of uncertainty as to which twin they were. Only half of his fraternal twins said this. Six twins were unable to tell their own voices apart on a recorder.[1]

He was surprised how infrequently pranks occurred among them. "Perhaps the rarity of switching in this way arises because they fear losing an individual identity that is already tenuous enough in some pairs."

When he asked how they felt if a stranger addressed them by their twin's name, most of them said they didn't try to correct it. A few became angry—"almost as if the attitude was, 'Don't try to mix me up—I know who I am!' "

To the question how they would have reacted to being triplets, there were two principal replies: There would have been more conflict, for two would have paired off, and the public attention could be annoying.

Problems of Twinship

One adult male in his thirties with whom we ourselves talked was emphatic about the unhappiness of twinship. "I wouldn't live my childhood over for anything," Herb told us. "I hated it! My twin was the life of the party. I felt as if I had no name. I was just The Twin."

Underneath Herb was always timid. He and Hal dressed exactly alike, played in a band together, and were in the same squadron of the air force. Yet in school they alternated; first he led and his brother was the dud, then their roles were reversed. And in final exams they often switched identities. In college Herb was shy. He'd have a beer and ask a girl for a date. Then he'd lose his nerve when Saturday night came, and Hal would take the girl out.

"My twin and I were very close. I never fought with Hal—but I often fought for him. In a way I used him as a crutch, but now sometimes I'm his crutch."

His twin went to Mexico to get his medical degree. "I'm the thrifty one—Hal was always sending back for dough, and I'd give him a thousand or two."

Herb's biggest marital problem is his twin. His wife feels she has to compete with Hal for Herb's affection (and no doubt for dollars!). Their wives are very different types. To us it seemed odd that this more introverted twin had been the healthier one at birth while his brother was a "blue baby."

Another male identical reported that when the hospital phoned that his wife had had their first baby, it was his twin he rushed to see—not his wife!

Art Farmer, Negro jazz trumpeter and flügelhornist, lost his identical twin, Addison, several years ago. "Being a twin is not always a happy thing," he said. "I guess it's a resentment at being regarded as a twin, not an individual—as a part, not a whole.

"But when my brother died I felt—and still do—that part of me was gone. Next to being compared, the worst thing about having a twin is for him to die. We would have our fallings out, but if any real crisis ever came, we would discuss it and do whatever was necessary. We talked a lot. Even now, when I think of something, my first impulse is to tell Addison about it. If a person went to bed with two arms and woke up with one, he would know what I mean."[2]

Foursomes

Very unusual among twins are the foursomes—identical girls married to identical boys. We have two such sets among our correspondents. Ruby Salm is a retired nurse in Colorado, and her twin, Ruth, now widowed, teaches piano in a Kansas town while her son operates the huge farm. Ruth is also a serious exponent of astrology.

The sisters write each other daily. Ruby says: "Funny thing, when I get her letter, she asks me the same questions and talks about the same things she is reading right there in my letter! Our handwriting is very much alike, too. But if one is sick, we don't feel it beforehand.

"We went to high school with Ed and Ferd Salm. They were the best catches in town, and they felt that way about us, too! Papa had a hotel then and all the relatives were there for that big 'twins marry twins' wedding on August 12, 1930. It was written up all over the country.

"Ruth and I have had very happy marriages, so when some 'twin expert' stated in a magazine that twins shouldn't marry twins, I got mad enough to write him. He sent back long forms to fill out and asked for photographs, full and side face! It would have taken hours, and the boys wouldn't bother. But he was sure wrong! Ruth and I got the very best men ever born!"

From astrologer Ruth we learned that all four are Pisceans—the women February 26, the men March 18—but the girls and their husbands were born in different years, in Cimarron, Kansas. Ruby is older than Ruth by fifteen minutes, which Ruth says makes their charts quite different and accounts for her own widowhood. Ruby has 29 Virgo rising, with Ruth 2 Libra. Virgo explains Ruby's nursing, her passion for cleanliness and collecting antiques—pewter, glass, animals, clocks, and beautiful colored lamps about which she lectures. Lucky Jupiter rules Ruby's home; while for Ruth, Saturn puts more sadness there. Each couple had a boy and a girl.

In the very beginning of our correspondence, learning of Ruth's interest in astrology, we sent her a birth date alone with no details. She replied: "This person has had a hard life with much sadness, a sick and ailing mother, and from Saturn—ruling the bones—it was probably arthritis."

Did this fit the facts? She could hardly have been more accurate! The mother died at eighty-three, after forty years in a wheelchair, from arthritis.

In one letter Ruby wrote: "I can't imagine not ever being a twin. It would be a great void, a terrible loss. We bear our joys and sorrows together, have so much fun!"

"The Loveless Twins"

Through the International Twins Club we located an earlier foursome. Married in 1919, "The Loveless Twins"—as they were publicized during their ten years as a singing quartet on former chautauqua circuits—are very far from loveless. Starting with a double honeymoon, for over fifty years these four identical twins have had *one house, one car, and one bank account!*

Lela and Lola Teague and Harmon S. and Herman M. Loveless were born and reared just eight miles apart near Carthage, Missouri. They paired off by their voices, the boy with the lower voice picking the girl to match it.

After they left the chautauqua the men, as veterinary-medicine graduates, worked in the same United States Bureau of Animal Husbandry office for years until their retirement to Colorado Springs. They have no children, but knowing they'd all pick the same child, they gave up the idea of adoption after they failed to locate twin babies.

They all agree that they "wouldn't trade places with any nontwin" they know. Four heads and four hearts can work anything out, and when one of them starts laughing, nobody can have the blues for long.

Still vigorous and healthy in their seventies, they enjoy the twin conventions and are not fireside sitters. In fact, apologizing for a two-week delay in answering our inquiry, the men said they had gone deer-hunting, then taken their wives back to the Ozarks to see the autumn leaves.

Perhaps there is something special about that Colorado air, for here is another twins-marry-twins case where the couples own a home together. Herbert and Delbert Chase, identical twins of Thornton, Colorado, married the Sweet identical sisters in a double wedding in 1954. The first couple has a son and the second a daughter. Their picture is among the illustrations in this book.

Judy and Julie Wouldn't Change

Girls seem to enjoy twinship more than boys. Judy Stillwagon and Julie Kirk, who have volunteered to answer questions on the International Twins Club, are still inseparable. Their long letter is condensed here:

We were "only" children and believe this will cause twins to be closer. We never really cared if we had other close friends or not, which worried our mother. When Rolland and I [Judy] decided we'd like to get married, we told Julie if she could find someone she really loved, we would wait, and that is just what happened.

We had a formal wedding, went on our honeymoons together and stayed in the same cottage—and are all still together after twenty-two years! Julie and Jack have three boys and Rolland and I have two boys. Naturally we would have loved twins! Perhaps our boys will be fortunate that way. We always see each other three times a week, though now we live about twenty minutes' drive apart.

Though we can't explain it, we have been even more identical since we married. We've been going to the International Twins Convention for twenty-one years. We love to travel and really "play up" being twins! We have always dressed alike and *still do!*

During our dating years we usually double-dated. We wonder now what those boys thought, especially if one didn't want to double . . . they did it anyway! A lot of times they couldn't tell us apart, so Julie and I would grab the one we were with. I'm sure the boys at times would wonder, "Am I still with the one I started with?"

Ha! No, we never switched, since *we* never thought we looked that much alike. The boys would get a kick out of everyone looking and talking about the twins. Maybe it made them feel a little more important.

Every once in a while the gruesome thought goes through my mind and hers, too—*what will we do* when the time comes for one of us to be taken away? This is really horrible to us and we try to blank it from

our minds. We keep kidding that we'll go to the Old Folks Home hand
in hand, dressed alike!

Our husbands for years have been jealous thinking we really preferred being with each other than with them. But after twenty-two
years they are getting immune to the fact that we *have* to be together.
They do try to understand but sometimes can't seem to go along with
all our togetherness. They have been very good to us and our only
quarrels have been over this.

We often wonder how some people can stand being just *one* person.
For the rest of our lives we'll make the most of it. We are sorry for
any twins who are miserable, because they really were so lucky to be
of a multiple birth.

The Rowe Twins

The Rowe girls are models and photographers. Several years ago
they narrowly escaped death in an automobile crash and underwent
several operations. Recently they wrote us:

Now we are more identical than ever! Five years ago LaVelda had
exploratory surgery and was left with a long, crooked scar. This year
the doctors teased LaVona just before her own surgery and asked
what side of the navel her scar curved.

"Doctors, you've just got to be kidding!"

"No, you're identicals and believe in being just alike. We're going
to match up those scars!"

And they did just that. I now have the same scar LaVelda has!
My operation may have been the result of an accident when Sis was
thrown into me in the car. If so, I don't mind the surgery a bit, as
her being thrown into me saved her life. I'd rather lose a gallbladder
any day than my twin!

Twin Interdependence

During his famous early twin research Dr. H. H. Newman wrote:

The feeling of incompleteness when apart is said by many twins to
be very real and quite irresistible. Some of you . . . will recall the
extensively publicized case of a pair of one-egg twin musicians in
England. One of these twins died. The survivor tried for a year to live
alone, but it was seemingly impossible, for he committed suicide. From

his diary we learn that he suffered an unbearable feeling of incompleteness. He felt that only half of him was alive.

Theodore Roosevelt, writing to Professor Newman about his own interest in twins, mentioned the Cromwell girls of New York. During World War I they had been doing canteen work among the soldiers in France. Apparently the tragedies they encountered at the front were too much for them, for while returning home by ship they jumped overboard together into the ocean and were drowned.

Dr. James Shields (and other scientists) suggests that the close feeling multiples have for each other is partly biological and is determined by the physical makeup. Finding forty-four pairs of twins reared apart, he used a control group of twins brought up together for comparison. Some of his control pairs revealed familiar twin problems:

"I sometimes wonder if we had been parted more," one girl said, "if I would have had more self-confidence and been able to make up my own mind about things easily. I wonder if this is because I'm a twin?" Her sister, writing in a very similar script, says, "I . . . have always remained mediocre in everything, never really shone. The main reason I know is lack of confidence in myself. I cannot decide whether this is just the way I was born, or because I had a very happy sheltered life as a child. . . . or is it anything to do with being a twin?" Dr. Shields found the leader was more apt to get into difficulties, whereas the more restrained twin made a happier life adjustment.

In Philadelphia Mr. and Mrs. Fred Berrier, Jr., have twin boys, Terry and Jerry. "Jerry has been blind since he was a baby," his mother says, "but at times the twins react to things as one person. . . . At no time does Jerry's blindness prevent him from enjoying life."

When people ask if Jerry doesn't become a burden, "they're always surprised when we tell them he certainly isn't," she adds. "In fact, it seems that Terry sometimes depends on Jerry more than the other way around. When Jerry is not here, Terry seems almost lost."[3]

On the opposite side of the world the attitude of twins is opposite, too. In Japan the second twin is called the elder! Was he not mature and courteous enough to permit his partner to precede him through the door of life? Because he is the older, noblesse oblige confers upon him all the rights and obligations accorded to that station. And he takes the role very seriously—often with a weighty sense of his own importance.[4]

Akira Kawasaki, a Tokyo University psychologist who has specialized in twins, says: "The elder brother will volunteer to apologize when they break a window or will act as the negotiator." At the high school supported by the university there are 120 sets of twins. During junior and senior high-school years the twins are observed and tested by many experts in the educational field.

"We divide each set of twins and put them in separate classes so we can study the effects of different surroundings on them," said Kawasaki. "When they come here, we tell them that they were born at the same time, but will die separately, and we encourage them to think and act independently. When they first come here, they tend to be very much alike, but gradually they develop their own personalities."

Dr. Helen L. Koch, professor emeritus of psychology at the University of Chicago, goes into the study in depth in her book *Twins and Twin Relations*.[5] She found that the closer the twinship, the less frequent such problems as stuttering. Fraternal twins are more apt to be jealous, and boy twins have a harder time than girls, she agrees. (Even in the womb boys are more active and competitive.) She found them moodier, with a stronger tendency toward revenge, teasing, and projecting blame.

Twin girls were more cheerful than singletons in her control group, probably because they were showered with more attention and parents tried harder to show no favoritism. Her opposite-sex pairs were somewhat more subdued. The boy (often frailer) was apt to be henpecked and feel inferior, because girls gain height faster and are brighter at one period. He has fewer friends among boys, yet is often rejected by the sister and her friends. The sister may be ashamed of his slowness, be critical and a tattler. Yet even so, the boy does not want separation and feels deserted.

But boy-girl pairs probably develop greater understanding of the opposite sex. And regardless of sex, dominance as "leaders" often shifts among all twins. Also, one twin may dominate at home, another at school. Dominance seems less pronounced with identicals.

Identicals and Fraternals—Behavioral Factors

All twins are more victimized by comparisons than are single children. They are expected to be alike, and if one falls behind, very damaging ego wounds may result.

"What are the ramifications," Dr. Koch asks, "of constant urging or pressuring of twins to be different, to be themselves, or conversely to be alike and devoted?" (Also, what are the parents' real motives? Is it, at rock bottom, their own glory?) "May not an identical twin be best expressing his individuality when he is most like his co-twin, since the two have identical genes?" she suggests.

What does it do to a child to be forced into the role of a prima donna, to sound alike, dress alike? Yet many twins told Dr. Koch they enjoyed this element, since it got them more attention. And twins who stopped dressing alike often resumed it just for this reason.

She found there was great prestige value in being an identical twin. When both were enrolled in the same class, they tended to be more popular, not only from the distinction but perhaps through relying on the other's social support. She felt that there should be no routine handling as to separation in school. There was so much dogma and personal opinion in this area that it was all dubious and hard to separate cause and effect.

Sometimes being in the same class stimulated both to achieve more, but at other times the superiority of one child overpowered the other's self-confidence. She (and other psychologists) stated that any rigid ruling by the school administration is a great error. Each case is different and should be decided separately after experiment.

Twins put into separate rooms could react with traumatic shock, much like devoted wives who lose their husbands. They may spend most of the time staring out of the window "always wondering where my brother is."

Female identicals contrast strongly with males in having more interests, social involvement, and popularity. But Dr. Koch found nonidentical girls to be the most outgoing and vivacious of all the classifications. Perhaps here each felt that her sister's differing gifts supplemented her own and bolstered any weaknesses. They were wholly themselves yet still not alone—a united front in any crisis.

In a three-year study of 150 sets of twins for the National Institute of Mental Health, Dr. Eve Lazar pointed out marked differences in the problems of identicals and fraternals.

One of her twins, four-year-old Fran, rushed to the mirror with bitter tears. "I'm Fran!" she shouted angrily. "I look like Fran. Why can't they see I'm Fran? Why do they call me Sally!" At these times the feeling of having no separate identity hurts and bewilders identicals.

Fraternals are particularly competitive and intensely jealous rivals, especially when one is markedly different in abilities. Almost all of Dr. Lazar's male fraternals were badly upset because their twin sisters were bigger. If parents realize this is normal, they can take extra pains to try to keep the boys from feeling small and inadequate.

By understanding that identicals and fraternals will differ in definite, and predictable, ways parents can eliminate much stress. The fraternals may be in a constant state of war through jealous rivalry, but since they are just as unlike as single brothers and sisters, equal performance should never be expected. The identicals, on the contrary, may be too close, with constant confusion as to which is which.

One of Dr. Lazar's pairs still recalls with anguish the summer they were told they would be separated at junior high school and were plagued by constant nightmares. And a woman who is today a great success in her profession said she was always "the dull twin." Not till her sister went to college was she able for the first time to be herself, with no worries over comparisons. Then she came into her own, and the twin who went to college was delighted by her sister's success.

Twins learn fast to exploit their sameness, to show off, to rule the roost, and just as much harm can come from this behavior. Though the problem differs, the solution is the same: Assure each child that he is equally loved and that he is loved for his uniqueness. Never compare—and never punish both when you don't know which is to blame.

It seems likely that becoming used to the special closeness and sharing with a twin may often be good training for those qualities later on in marriage. Dr. Charlotte Taylor, a biochemist with postdoctoral work in psychology, studied the marriages of fifty twin couples (twenty-five foursomes) at U.C.L.A. She chose twins for research on marriage stability because they have so much in common and their physical makeup is similar.

Dr. Taylor hypothesizes that stable marriages result where couples are compatible on the chemical level. Twins' marriages usually turn out in similar fashion—either happily or in a breakup. Rarely would one succeed and the other fail. Dr. Taylor found the divorce rate much lower with her pairs—only 12 percent compared to California's usual 50 percent.

Happiness among Siamese Twins

Even Siamese twins can enjoy their twinship. While genetically identical, they may not be so in appearance. The Gibbs Sisters of vaudeville days were unlike in many qualities. Mary was only four feet eight, overweight, easygoing, and carefree. Margaret, two inches taller, was thin, high-strung, and worried about health and finances.

At sixteen they went into show business with a song-and-dance act in the United States and in Europe. They retired in 1941 and started a gift shop in their birthplace, Holyoke, Massachusetts.

They came to prefer their condition and refused all offers of an operation. To them it would have been an amputation.

"We are perfectly happy as we are!" they insisted.

And so they remained. When they died at fifty-four, they requested burial together in a special coffin, with no autopsy.

The Story with Quads and Quints

Plenty of twin lives, even grievously handicapped ones, prove that it doesn't have to be "Scrappy Birthday to You!" In spite of the extra emotional and psychological demands upon multiples, many of them escape without sad hang-ups—perhaps proving what the philosophers have said for centuries, that character is destiny.

Even quads and quints can come through it all with fair serenity. We have the Diligentis of Argentina, for whom their father's millions as well as his common sense provided balanced lives. Yet without riches but with an equal amount of common sense, the Pinkham quads of Standish, Maine, seem to be a happy lot of individualists.

When they were thirteen, their mother, Mrs. Silas E. Pinkham, said: "Never, never call them quadruplets. They are four entirely separate and distinct individuals."

That year (1966) they were eighth-graders in the local junior high school. Jane won the science prize for her insect exhibit. Melissa collected rocks but was planning to be a nurse. Roberta, the only girl with bobbed hair, loved reading and records. They accused the boy, William, of "hogging the ball" when they played baseball.

"But they'll scratch and bite to get it away!" he retorted. He enjoyed carpentry and helped his father build their little white Cape Cod cottage.

There is a strong family resemblance, but they all vary in height, and the girls have always chosen different clothes and hair styles.

Their mother is a strict but kind disciplinarian. "We sleep dormitory style. The girls and I share one large room and the menfolk take another. To speed the morning lineup for the bathroom, the girls each have a mirror for primping in the kitchen."

However, in Castle Combe, England, the Good quadruplets— Jennifer, Bridget, Frances, and Elizabeth—all agreed at their twenty-first birthday reunion that they disliked being quads.

Elizabeth, now a nurse in a Boston children's hospital, said, "I left home two and a half years ago to work in America. Basically I never liked being a quad and wanted to get away."[6]

Her sister Jennifer agreed. "Everybody in school hated us and hit us for no reason at all except just because we were quads. It was awful! And there was this dreadful business of dressing in the same clothes. We stopped that the moment we could. We so desperately wanted to be individuals and not thought of as quads!"

A famous set of Negro girls, the Fultz quads, have also had a hard time from their relationship. They were born in Reidsville, North Carolina, on May 23, 1946. Their home was a sharecropper's shack with seven older brothers and sisters, their mother, Annie (who had been left a deaf-mute at two by spinal meningitis), and their fifty-nine-year-old father. Almost immediately they became the best-cared-for, most famous black babies in the world.

The Pet Milk Company offered to pay all their medical bills and hire a nurse in exchange for publicity pictures. When they were about ten, their nurse, Mrs. Saylor, legally adopted them. Later, through an employee of the company, the girls got a scholarship at Bethune-Cookman College in Florida.

It might have been better if they could have gone to separate schools, for they did not know how to live except as a unit. Other students found them standoffish. They cut classes, and even when the college worked out a special program to help them, they still didn't attend. Musically gifted, they spent their time "waiting for a break."

The Saylors, who love and believe in the girls, finally decided the South was holding them back. Mr. Saylor gave up his job, and the family moved in two cars to Peekskill, New York. They found a pleasant apartment near a relative, but, as stated in *Ebony,* they are "grown up, disappointed and bitter" and haven't wanted to know anybody there.

They are attempting to get into television with their musical talents. "We're still going to be big stars," they told *Ebony* writer Charles L. Sanders.[7]

Perhaps because of the accident of birth and the fanfare of publicity that followed, they developed somewhat unrealistic goals and never quite came down to earth. The Pet Milk Company says they are only one among many sets sponsored over the years. The average got no more than ten thousand dollars in all, but the Fultz girls were "sort of special," got much more than that, and were carried along into their teens long after they had no advertising value to the company.

Dr. Helen Koch may be right when she suggests that parents discover their own motives for making a big deal of multiples. Is it to feed their own vanity or really to enjoy duplicate delights? In this connection we quote a letter we received from a mother who never had a twin:

> We mothers of singles wonder why mothers with twins think of themselves as more special than the rest of us. Conversations with them are most boring. That is *all* they talk about, and their poor little nontwins sit there on the sidelines with the saddest faces!
>
> Babies come into the world naked, but mothers of twins immediately *make* them different and apart, by putting identical garments on each twin, identical beds. Everything possible in their first formative years is a repetition. Then these same mothers have the gall to sit there and tell you, "We think of them as individuals and never call them the twins!"
>
> God made all mothers and children and I doubt He expected this earthly bid for prestige. The character of a child is set in those years prior to school. How sad for twins to be always duplicated! When you suggest that it is really Mama who must live in the limelight, because naturally the little ones couldn't care less about dressing alike, they look at you as if you've lost your marbles. They cannot see themselves as others see them—conceited, unfair to their other children, publicity-crazy. We have several in our neighborhood and get a chuckle at the ends they go to to be noticed as something important.

This letter is harsh, but there is some truth to it. Some of the poor little multiples such as the Genains (Chapter 5) would hardly have been hidden away for life in an institution if they had not been forced into the prima-donna role from birth—and only because of the circumstances of birth. Too much was expected of them, until they became pathetic puppets who could only retreat. We question whether the least neurotic of singletons, dropped into that sick environment for twenty-five years, could have emerged a happy and productive person.

It should be recognized that the arrival of twins accentuates any tensions, sexual or otherwise, already in the home—and that some mothers who were not emotionally satisfied in childhood now pour their disappointment into those infant marvels, the new multiples, with unfortunate psychological damage.

One of our famous twins, columnist Ann Landers, often receives mail from youngsters who are experiencing difficulties with their peers or in their own homes. Many times the tensions and stresses can be traced back to the parents themselves. To one concerned member of a pair of troubled twins, she wrote:

> Your parents are making a big mistake. You girls should not be exploited as if you were joined at the hip. Twins ought to be treated as two separate human beings. Their individual tastes and talents should be respected and encouraged. I hope your parents will permit you to break up this vaudeville act. Duplicates on display may be good for *their* ego, but to you and your sister it means only double trouble.[8]

Warm and gifted parents, or those whose fairy godmothers deal them forty-six "happy" chromosomes out of the thousands available "in the broth," will find multiples a quick, though expensive way to a big, loving family. But at other times it calls upon all the courage and wisdom they possess. And with the fathers it certainly separates the men from the boys in very short order.

Among these children, as close together as two ticks of the clock, the many twists of twindom can be tricky indeed, and even murder is not an unknown climax. Too much "vitamin I" is bad for anybody. Sometimes the leader needs his follower even more than the other way around, and deep inside he may be desperately dependent.

The Nicholson Twins

A tragic case of wavering between love and hate for each other resulted when the young heir of the Pullman car and Cudahy meatpacking fortunes shot his twin to death in Los Angeles in December, 1964. Deprived of a father early and with little love from a quarrelsome, embittered mother, these boys had small sense of security or even identity.

Todd and Timothy Nicholson were born just two minutes apart on August 2, 1942, in Tulsa, Oklahoma. Nobody ever distinguished between them. Even their mother called them both "Tim-Todd" and knew them apart only because Tim was left-handed. They had no one but each other to be close to, and a good part of the time they couldn't stand each other. Violent, erratic, and erotic, they made a game of seducing each other's girls. When he killed his brother, Timothy did not even know which of them had fathered "his" child. In this atmosphere of violent competition they wrangled and parleyed their inheritance into a very considerable fortune.

Their mother was an Irish girl from an upstate Michigan farm. Like her father, also a twin, she was a heavy drinker, and she snatched at the chance to marry into a rich Chicago family.

But the boys' father soon left her. Twins, he said, gave him the creeps! When she divorced him and moved to California, a monthly check came from a trust fund. Resentful of her "burden," she shipped the seven-year-old boys off to military school. The other cadets promptly dubbed them "T 'n T."

For a brief period their father took them back but soon showed his boredom. Return to their mother only resulted in a different kind of brawl when her lover beat one of them bloody.

Remorseful then, Roberta gave the boys driving lessons in the dark through a cemetery—"with headstones and vaults and winged statues of angels for road signs." They were eleven years old!

Of the two, Todd was the more violent, unpredictable, and unstable. He would go into the same blind rages that afflicted his mother —described by Tim as being like a twister coming with nobody knowing where it would hit. And Todd's rages would go on for hours until he dropped in exhaustion.

They had no allowances, for their mother spent all their money on herself. But they were not lazy. By working at long, hard, dirty jobs in radiator shops and the like, they earned enough to keep themselves in sports cars.

Just before their eighteenth birthday their father's death brought them about $250,000 each—either at twenty-one or earlier if they married. Although they were intensely competitive and battled constantly, they could not tolerate long separations from each other. Their quarrels and their devotion were equally necessary halves of the ugly, unstable pattern of their lives.

Todd attempted suicide, and both apparently tried to insure the other secretly for a million dollars. They had to outdo each other in business, where both found it easy to triple their money in short order. Todd would pistol-whip Tim in his rages to prove that Tim was the kid brother (with two minutes' difference in their ages!), but Tim no longer fought back. Todd's tearful outbursts and admissions of envy made him feel at fault.

When Timothy shot and killed his twin with a rifle on December 7, 1964, the evidence was conflicting. Was it really self-defense or the last straw after twenty-two years of seesawing emotions? He was sentenced to one to ten years and released after only three. The judge had said, "This is the tragic aftermath of two emotionally unstable youngsters receiving too much money. We all feel sorry for this defendant, who is the victim of circumstances to some extent."

Their twinship was not mentioned. Was that two minutes the decisive factor—or would two years' difference, given the same parents and upbringing, still have resulted in murder? After his release, Tim married his brother's fiancée, who had faithfully visited him throughout the period of his imprisonment.[9]

The Other Side of the Coin

Nevertheless, boy twins can be pals instead of enemies. Colonel Joseph Gerard and Colonel Gerard Joseph Gefell are both United States Army chaplains and monsignors of the Roman Catholic Church. They were together as airborne paratroopers in Alaska and later served in Vietnam. Now back in the United States, they get together whenever they can to go fishing or sky-diving. Both say they enjoy army life and feel needed there. Both received medals from the government of South Vietnam.

But of all our male pairs probably the closest were Judge Charles S. Crail, of Los Angeles, author of *My Twin Joe,* and his brother, whose experience in translating Latin word for word we discussed in Chapter 1.

When they grew up, they shared the same law office. Their handwriting was so alike that office workers couldn't distinguish between them. They lived a mile apart on the same bus line and always boarded the same bus and wore identical suits without prearrangement, so that regular passengers made a game of it.

Once Joe wired Charlie from Washington to meet him at the Republican Convention in Kansas City to nominate Herbert Hoover. The telegram was the only word Charlie received in California, but from opposite parts of the country the twins got on trains arriving in Kansas City at the same time. Dressed in exactly similar suits, hats, shirts, and ties, they found each other "as easily as homing pigeons" in the immense crowd.

Earlier, when they were young soldiers fighting in Cuba in the Spanish-American War, Charlie had a strange experience. Yellow fever was raging, and Joe was stricken. When Joe was hospitalized, Charlie could not sleep but suffered along with his twin until near dawn he slipped into deep sleep. Then he woke in terror.

In a vivid dream he had seen them both standing in the stern of a large ship in midocean, watching the foam in the wake. Then a tremendous wave washed Joe away. Charlie threw him a line, saw his face grow livid, mottled black as in yellow fever—then watched the strands of the rope parting while the breath seemed sucked out of his own body.

The next night the dream came twice, and on the third and fourth nights he kept flashing awake between successive nightmares. Only one frail strand remained of the rope. How could it hold? But the fifth night he slept dreamlessly. When he visited the hospital, he learned that Joe had passed the crisis.

In his story of their lives the judge wrote:

> It seems to me there is one point about identical twins which psychologists have left out of their book: there are willing twins and reluctant twins. Willing twins are pleased, proud and joyous in their twinsomeness, tenaciously clinging to their oneness.
>
> For such twins there are two laughs for one joke, two thrills for the same joy, and a double pain from the dagger thrust of sudden treachery. . . . It is a lot of fun to be a twin. In their relations with one another twins follow implicitly the Golden Rule, and this brings a bit of heaven down to earth. . . .
>
> It is happiness just to live when one is born a twin.

11 GEMINI AND THE OCCULT

> There is truth in palm reading, phrenology, and the signs of the zodiac—although I do not "believe" in any of them. There is truth in sunspots, diets, and handwriting analysis. You name it, no matter how silly it may sound, and if enough people have believed in it over a period of time, there is bound to be a residual core of truth in it. . . .
>
> Our task as humans is not to accept or reject any idea in toto but to discriminate, to select, to find that usable portion of truth in tenets we cannot fully believe in.

This statement was made by Sydney J. Harris, nationally syndicated columnist, after reading that a report given before the American Academy of Pediatrics revealed that some doctors were now diagnosing certain diseases of childhood from the lines in their palms.

Although librarians shelve serious works on the hand side by side with those dealing with fortune-telling, we will ignore the latter. In the serious volumes we have uncovered information on left-handed children and on the so-called simian line on the palm, both of which are fairly frequent with twins. Some doctors now feel they can make "an absolute and positive diagnosis" of mongolism from the palms of these children.

The simian line (so called from being a characteristic of monkeys' palms) is a *single* heavy line running width-wise across the hand instead of the usual two parallel lines.

But if parents see this line in their twins' hands, they should not

146

leap to frightening conclusions without further evidence. Its presence, however, does seem to indicate a high-strung and unpredictable personality. Fred Gettings speaks of it as of great importance to psychologists, anthropologists, and doctors. "The simian line has many forms and many degrees," he writes. It is not common in its pure form. Some hands having this heavy line belong to creative people, religious fanatics, or, in coarser palms, criminal types.

In such twins and singletons the encouragement to develop creative outlets will be of tremendous value. Novelist Vicki Baum is said to have had this line in modified form.[1]

Twins and Graphology

If appearance, voice, character, and even events can be so alike with twins, what about their handwriting? In the United States graphology has been cheapened by "parlor trick" entertainers, but genuine handwriting analysis is neither "psychic" nor chatty humor. A skilled graphologist's deep analysis of a disturbed person should no more be shown to that person than the psychiatrist's private report.

Sir Francis Galton, the father of modern genetics, had a low opinion of graphology because he found only one pair of twins with similar writing, but in his day it was not possible to differentiate MZ and DZ. Newman treated handwriting and graphology seriously and fairly. In his book written in collaboration with Freeman and Holziner he reproduced the writing of most of his pairs of twins, saying that although he did not regard graphology as scientifically established, there was some basis to the conclusion that character was revealed in writing. The differences shown in the personalities of his twins were often such as seemed to be suggested by their writing.

Regarding the Genain quadruplets, whose story we related in Chapter 5, Dr. David Rosenthal discussed the clinic's remarkable analyst, who was given samples written by the four girls. She was able to match each one to samples made eleven to twelve years later and made some striking hits as to their difficulties from their papers alone. Yet she never saw the girls and knew only that schizophrenia was the diagnosis. Her comment was that all four girls had originally had adequate psychophysical resources but had been drained by emotional tensions and stresses that resulted in breakdowns.[2]

Other psychologists have made a deep study of the subject. Dr.

Werner Wolff, who after escaping from the Nazis became a professor of psychology at Bard College, Annandale-on-Hudson, New York, wrote a scholarly book describing the scope of such analyses.

In his *Diagrams of the Unconscious* he said:

> I am conscious of the fact that this most promising field of investigation is in its beginnings so that it is fully as difficult to cope with the exaggerated skepticism of scientists who expect from handwriting less than from any rat running blindly through a maze, as with the exaggerated expectations of the laymen who expect everything.[3]

The English graphologist and psychologist Dr. Robert Saudek said that after an exhaustive study of the writing of twins, he had found some identicals who wrote so much alike that even he could not distinguish between them.

Occasional twins (and singletons) disturb their parents by writing backward, and in consequence some who really have high IQs are misdiagnosed as retarded or otherwise abnormal. Actually such children may really have what is called "cross dominance"—they are predominantly right-handed but left-eyed. Children who do such mirror-writing should always be tested for this condition. Sometimes emotional problems are present or develop because of the accompanying frustrations. Special training will correct the trouble. Winston Churchill and Leonardo da Vinci, notoriously poor students, may have had this problem. Leonardo drew with his left hand and painted with his right.

By contrast to the informed approach of trained analysts, meager results are achieved by those psychologists who attempt to assess similarities in writing with no knowledge of valid rules for such judgment. Although this is no more scientific than amateur diagnosis between MZ and DZ twins, some of these men even pride themselves on inventing their own rules!

Torsten Hüsen in his *Psychological Twin Research* told his raters —primary-school teachers and graduate students—to pay *no attention* to slope, letter height, and connecting strokes. Yet these are among the primary indications in graphology. His subsequent comment that his raters each "apparently used different frames of reference, applied different standards of judgment when grading similarity" seems naïve. Obviously quite unconscious that he himself had defeated his own purpose, he spoke of handwriting analysis as having "low reliability."[4]

But other researchers who are not handwriting analysts have found many likenesses in the writing of twins. Dr. Helen Koch at the University of Chicago and Dr. James Shields mentioned a number of identicals whose writing was very similar.

It would seem from these cases that researchers who attempt to assess the reliability of any of the more unconventional methods of analysis should remain totally objective. They should be willing to acknowledge that rules do exist within even off-beat disciplines. Unless they make some use of its frame of reference, they have not tested the method but merely (unknowingly) themselves.

Twins and Astrology

Readers who share the current interest in astrology may think they have the real answer to the mystery of twins. And possibly they may—in part. To investigate such claims, we have corresponded with many astrologers in the United States and abroad and have studied their journals, uncovering a large amount of data on twins and on those who merely share the same birth date.

If the hour of birth is not known, astrologers "rectify" (an educated guess) or set a sun chart for the day itself. Astrologers say persons born on the same day will have some things in common, because the relationship among the sun and planets will be fundamentally the same.

But an accurate individual horoscope is set for the birth moment and the latitude and longitude on the earth at the place of birth. Here the sun and planets would be differently posited for each individual wheel-like chart, according to how the heavenly bodies rose and set during the twenty-four hours. A child born in one country at noon has the sun high in the sky (and in his chart); one born at that precise moment on the opposite side of the globe would be born at midnight, sun at nadir. These differing placements give different meanings and influences.

One of Hitler's so-called occult staff, Karl Krafft, was an eccentric who finally died in a concentration camp after doing much astrological research for the Nazis. Early in his career he compiled an impressive list from the civil registers of Basel and Geneva, Switzer-

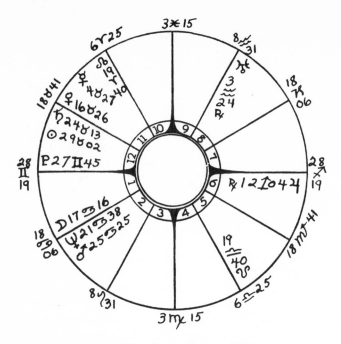

The Gibbs Sisters, Siamese Twins

Horoscope of the Gibbs Sisters, Siamese twins, born at 6:30 A.M. true local mean time, on May 20, 1912, in Holyoke, Massachusetts. A "marked" chart because of fixed stars (Pleiades) on the Sun, and (Algol) on Saturn. Pluto—here malefic ruler of the 6th House of Health—is exactly on the Ascendant in the double-bodied Twin Sign, Gemini. The Sun, in the critical 29th degree, is in the 12th House of Sorrows with Saturn. The harsh conjunction of Moon, Neptune, and Mars in the 2d House of Money, but in good aspect to the Sun, Saturn, and Venus, gave power to earn through the sorrow.

In Siamese charts fantastic Neptune usually afflicts the Sun, Moon (as here), or Ascendant, with double-bodied signs occupying sensitive spots.

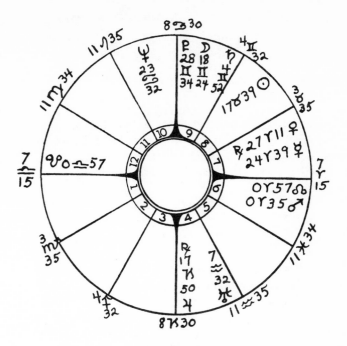

Teratoma Case

Case of a teratoma, or "included twin," which according to some
doctors begins as undeveloped cells from the patient's own twin
(not her child). Birth chart of a woman born at 3:10 P.M. on
May 8, 1913, at 41:48 north latitude, 89:42 west longitude. The
cells remained inert within her body for years, until stimulated after
the birth of several children. Diagnosed as a tumor, it proved to be
this fetal cyst. Surgery in 1935 was followed by ten other operations. Men can also have these growths.

Mars, planet of surgery, here is in the 6th House of Health and
exactly conjuncts the North Lunar Node, with the fixed star Difda;
while the Dragon's Tail (South Lunar Node) is right on the
Ascendant. All are in bad aspect to Pluto's critical degree. In this
second chart, too, Neptune adds mystery by making the physical
condition obscure and unique.

Chart used by permission of *Dell's
Horoscope* magazine.

land, showing how often those who shared the same birth *hour* died of the same cause at the same age.[5]

Cosmic Twins

We ourselves have unearthed some extraordinary cases of parallelism, not only of actual twins with near-identical lives such as we discussed in earlier chapters, but of persons from different families born on the same day, especially if in nearby locations.

Some examples:

A strange case of confusion in the British army came to light when Edward Patrick O'Connor was held fourteen days because authorities believed him to be Patrick James O'Connor, a deserter from the Royal Engineers. Army records showed both men were born in Dublin on March 14, 1944, and both had the same dental fillings and the same national insurance number.[6]

Two Swiss girls, Jacqueline Luscher and Elizabeth Boxxhard, were born in the same town in Switzerland on the same day, married on the same day, and moved to Los Angeles at the same time. There they both gave birth to baby girls in the same hospital on the same day, attended by the same physician.[7]

In neither the army nor the Swiss case is the birth time known. Each of these pairs had similar "sky patterns" and with close birth times, would also have had similar patterns in their individual horoscopes.

The (British) *Astrological Journal* gives another interesting case:

> Two unrelated women, both named Edna, met for the first time in a hospital in Hackensack, New Jersey. They were born on the same date and it was the first confinement for both. Their babies, too, were born at the same hour, with the same weight, and were given the same name. The fathers, both named Harold, were also born on the same date! The men were in the same business, owned a car of the same make, model and color. The couples had married on the same day. Physically the women were similar, with the same number of brothers and sisters, and had the same religion—which differed from that *shared* by the husbands. The family dogs were of the same sex and kind, obtained at the same time, and were given the same name— Spot.[8]

The same publication printed a striking photograph of two little girls born within five minutes of each other in the same hospital in White Plains, New York, on February 20, 1947—Jean Henderson and Joyce Ritter (pictured in this book). At about the age of six they moved next door to each other, to the great confusion of their neighbors, schoolmates, and teachers. The likeness was extraordinary, feature by feature, even to large upper incisors. Each family had five similar children, and the fathers had similar jobs at the same airport.

The *Journal* comments that such children may be more alike than real twins because they are not complementary halves. Little Jean and Joyce, for example, have their hair parts on the same, not on opposite, sides. Also, twins are never given the same names—but by strange coincidence, these "cosmic twins," as the magazine calls them, often are.

Perhaps even more outstanding, because the likeness concerned prominent careers, is the story of Professors Jans Jensen and Maria Goeppert-Mayer. They shared a Nobel Prize in physics and were engaged on practically identical work—a shell model of the universe. Each had worked independently, totally unaware of the other's activities, one in Germany, one in the United States. Their papers were published simultaneously. When the two scientists got in touch, they made an astonishing discovery.

They had been born on the same date in German towns that stood on the same latitude!

Similarly two other eminent scientists were born the same hour of the same day in different countries—Paul Heroult, of Thury, France, and Charles Hall, of Thompson, Ohio. Like the preceding case, each man invented precisely the same process, for producing aluminum.[9] Both died in the same year.

King George III, of England, had such a birth-mate, one James Hemming. In spite of their very different positions in life, there was a startling likeness in appearance and in the events of their lives. Hemming set up in business at the same time George III was crowned. Both were betrothed and married on the same days and died within the same hour.

Strangely, George III's son, the next ruler of England, repeated the coincidence. A chimney sweep was born the same day and hour as George IV, "the one wrapped in purple, the other rolled in sooty blankets," as an old book put it. Both lived profligate, reckless lives until their fortunes crashed simultaneously. The blood horses of the king and the donkeys of the sweep were sold for debts the same day!

But the following case, which also concerns royalty, is the most striking of all:

In the summer of 1901 King Umberto, of Italy, met the proprietor of a small restaurant in Monza while dining there and found that this dignified man with a great white moustache was his living image. To his even greater astonishment, the man's name was also Umberto. Both had been born March 14, 1844, at 10:30 A.M. in Turin; each married (also on the same day) a wife named Margherita and had an only son named Vittorio. On the day when the king was crowned, the other Umberto opened his restaurant. Both king and commoner had twice received medals for bravery on the same days.

Learning that the restaurant owner would be at the grandstand next day for an athletic event, the king decided to make him a Cavaliere of the Crown. But instead came the news that his "twin" had accidentally shot himself while cleaning his gun.

"How very sad!" the king exclaimed. "Find out when the funeral is held. I will attend in person."

The words had scarcely left his lips when three shots rang out, and two of the assassin's bullets pierced the king's heart.

Identicals with Strange Parallel Destinies

The preceding cases have involved nontwins. But there are astonishing cases of real twins born to the same parents and separated by circumstance.

Two astonishing cases of duplicate fates for twins separated at birth are reported by Joseph F. Goodavage.[10] When two poultry trucks collided in Miami, Florida, in June, 1961, the drivers proved to be identical twins—separated at birth but now living forty-five miles apart, having the same jobs and with wives of the same name. Here, too, the family dogs were alike, as were the sex and age of their children, and both men drove the same kind of truck.

But Goodavage's most eerie case of real twins is this: A Tucson doctor and his wife were sent to prison for extreme cruelty to an adopted child, five-year-old Tina. She was found bloody from beatings, cowering with her hands roped behind her, and emaciated beyond belief. The police had to protect the couple from outraged neighbors.

"At almost the same time but in another state, an identical story unfolded." A dentist and his wife had also beaten and abused an adopted five-year-old and kept her tied. They, too, were sentenced. While checking adoption records it was learned that the second child was Tina's twin, from whom she had been separated since infancy.

What enigmatic influence gave these little children similar and shocking destinies?

Jeff Mayo, who is a tutor for the Faculty of Astrological Sudies in London, sent us an autographed copy of his own text, *Teach Yourself Astrology*.[11] In it he writes:

> How does an astrologer account for the differences in twins born practically together?
>
> The Ascendant, indicative of very *individual* characteristics in the birth chart, changes its degree every four minutes, and the Ascending Sign could change within a single minute, introducing marked variations. Twins are sometimes born widely apart, causing appreciable differences. Even Siamese twins *must* differ. There is a "spiritual factor" in each one of us that cannot be interpreted through astrology. This is the source of free will; individuality in its truest sense. The birth chart is essentially the blue-print of the "Earth vehicle" through which the spirit of man incarnates.

During each twenty-four hours all twelve signs (of 30 degrees each), 360 degrees, will have crossed the horizon. But this does not mean that there will be a mere 360 types of personality, for each day the earth is moving one degree along its own orbit. So multiplying 360 by 365 days per year gives in itself 131,400 variations annually. Astrologers consider many other factors also, such as positions above and below the horizon and the constantly changing relations ("aspects") among the planets and "lights" (sun and moon). It is important also to know the *kind* of time in use at the birthplace (daylight saving, double war time, etc.).

Thus it is clear how preposterous the superstitious sun-sign readings of the newspapers and popular magazines become and why serious astrologers hold them in contempt.

The sun is only *one* factor out of all those mentioned above, and more. To say that all persons born within the entire thirty days that the sun remains in one sign will have certain characteristics and personality traits is like trying to make some precise diagnosis about the heart while ignoring the rest of the body.

We asked Mr. Mayo to explain the apparent inconsistency of ignoring the precession of the equinoxes (i.e., that the stars today are not in the same constellations as in the days of the Chaldeans).

"My opinion of the signs," he answered, "is that they don't refer to the constellations at all, but to a belt, a magnetic field of influence, surrounding, enveloping Earth—*within the Earth's own sphere of radiation.*"[12] (The *constellations* vary from about 22 degrees to over 31 degrees, whereas the *signs* are exactly 30 degrees each.)

Another well-known astrologer, George Cardinal LeGros, wrote us: "Mirror-image twins must be born within a few minutes of each other to have the same degree rising. If twins are not born within minutes they are not true identicals." (We find this latter statement given some support by a survey of fifteen hundred twins which was made at Birmingham University in England about 1950. They found identicals tended to be born closer together than fraternals.) LeGros continues: "Persons born in the same town on the same day-month-year-hour-minute have parallel destinies. That is, all major events are practically the same but in keeping with the social-economic status."

We know, too, that when twins are nonidentical the time of conception could differ; and the physical hazards of multiple births such as crowding in the womb and an oxygen lack can handicap one infant.

Key Period for Multiple Births

Statistics show that the period of late May to early June has the highest proportion of multiple births. Since these days fall in the zodiacal sign of Gemini, the fact that the ancients named Gemini "The Twins" suggests they were aware of this. All the ancient zodiacs symbolize this period by two figures—twin children in Europe and Mexico; a man and a woman in Peru; and two generals among the Mayans.

The Dionne quints were born not only in the sign of Gemini but with Gemini rising on the horizon. In fact astrologers mention that Dr. Dafoe himself was a Gemini, "capable in an emergency."

Carl Payne Tobey, mathematician-astrologer who distinguished himself by discovering the prime dendrite (the formula for prime numbers that mathematicians had been seeking since the days of Euclid), has written us several letters about twins. In one he says:

> Did twins start to breathe at the same moment? The ancients considered birth to be the moment when a child drew its first breath as a separate entity. Even if twins emerged at almost the same moment, this factor can vary. Long ago we convinced ourselves that a premature birth is every bit as legitimate astrologically as a natural birth moment, because that is when the child breathes and becomes separate from the mother.

A birth may take some five to ten minutes from the first appearance to the first cry. Many babies take much longer (if unassisted) and may even appear and retreat. The first cry may come even before the head of the baby has completely emerged.

A Scottish friend who is one of the mosaic, twin-within-a-twin persons described in Chapter 3 wrote us:

> Apparently I stuck my head out at 10 of midnight on the 30th, took one look, and decided NO! I was hauled out wrong-end-befront at 12:30 A.M. of the 31st. My mother happened to be in a coma due to quite another illness. As Scots law (being Roman) has never stated whether the time of birth is one's first appearance or the moment of separation from one's parent, I got a certificate saying 30th-31st. No astrologer by any of their many systems has *ever* set a chart that fitted me!

We learn that some astrologers will not touch the charts of either cesarean births or nonidentical twins, at least for predictions, saying "they don't work." But in response to a suggestion from a member of the American Federation of Astrologers, Washington, D.C., we wrote to her fellow-member, Miss Mary Peter, of Jonesboro, Illinois.

Miss Peter has her own method with twins' charts, unique so far as we can discover. In addition to the usual natal charts (almost identical for twins born within minutes), she erects a second chart for the second twin.

Twins are partners, she explains; thus for the second twin, the 7th

House, opposite the Ascendant, becomes the 1st House. This is because the 7th is called "the House of Marriage, open enemies and *partners.*" So for the last-born twin she does an extra, mirror-image chart—reversing the circle of twelve houses so that the 7th is put on the left where the firstborn's 1st House was. She claims that this chart works for predictions for the second twin and sent us many pages of complex explanations.

Perhaps her method will give astrologers a new theory for twins!

(Readers interested in her data for the Brodie Siamese twins will find it at the back of the book at the end of the notes for this chapter.)

No doubt many readers are saying, But is there *really* anything to astrology? Can't all this just be coincidence?

Well, certain skilled astrologers (not the bead-curtain variety) have taken some amazing tests. In these tests they distinguished, *from the birth moments alone,* given factors of profession, circumstances, etc. In one case in Germany, out of 2,370 answers, 83 percent were correct.

Another test was set by the late psychologist Vernon Clark, of Evanston, Illinois. Some astrologers in his panel achieved scores far beyond chance. In this difficult test the occupations cited were very close: owner of a snake farm and a veterinary doctor; an artist, an art teacher, and an art critic. Also paired were a medical librarian with a lifelong prostitute and madam, who were born on the same date with only five hours, and some degrees of latitude and longitude, to distinguish them. Yet his most competent astrologers came through the test above the laws of probability. One of them correctly identified seventeen out of the twenty birth moments! It would seem that such results as these must be achieved through rules that work.

"I think astrology was discovered mathematically and not through objective observation," Carl Payne Tobey wrote to us. "Things happen in a certain way because, mathematically, there is no other way." Elsewhere Tobey wrote:

> It is a strange fact that scientists searching for cycles in nature find cycles in almost anything, even in random numbers. Which implies that they are not random. In other words, there may be no such thing as random. Even that which appears to be random and chaotic may be in accord with some unknown design.[13]

The Sun, the Planets, and Human Biological Clocks

These ideas are thought-provoking. Scientists who accuse astrologers of childish egotism in thinking the stars are interested in their insignificant concerns are snared by their own frame of reference. The stars "couldn't care less!" The stars and man exist independently of each other, but both seem to be responding to the same cosmic rhythms.

But is it really possible that the sun, moon, and earth wind our biological clocks? And that they have some relationship to the physical and mental handicaps that afflict multiple births more than singletons?

Michel Gauquelin is a French statistician and scientist who is hostile to astrology. But his book *The Cosmic Clocks* contains some very astonishing data.[14] He tells of separate Italian and Japanese research involving thousands of experiments. "Man is a living sundial," he quotes the biologist Takata. Other scientists found that sunspot activity coincided with crises in certain diseases, including eclampsia, the dreaded convulsive poisoning in childbirth which takes the lives of many twins. Thus, said Gauquelin, astronomers—he doesn't mention astrologers!—could warn doctors "of the days when because of the sun's ill humor, women in labor need to be very closely watched."

Several American doctors have studied the moon's relation to birth. For many years it was graphed both in Los Angeles and in Tucson hospitals. In 1951 Dr. Eldon Webb Tice, chief obstetrician of the Methodist Hospital in Los Angeles, testified in court: "When we have a full moon, I know we are going to be rushed. It has been shown that when the natural feminine cycle *doesn't fit with the moon,* conception is very difficult."

In New York City Doctors Walter and Abraham Meneker, after checking the pattern of births for three years (about half a million babies), also find the full moon significant. Their report appeared in the *American Journal of Obstetrics and Gynecology:* "These conclusions also apply to conception. The human gestation period is nine lunar months—so that a child born under the full moon is likely to have been conceived at the same point in the lunar cycle."[15]

Dr. Leonard J. Ravitz, a neuropsychiatrist at Yale, studied a pair of male adult schizophrenic twins. At new and full moons they were always at their worst—shouting, preaching, threatening to "slay the wicked." At such times they had vivid dreams and tried to escape. "We are all electrical machines," Ravitz said.[16]

Sex Determination of Babies

Have moon phases anything to do with the sex of babies, as midwives' gossip has declared for centuries? In medieval days nostrums were sold to ensure a male heir. Today scientists know that the baby's sex is determined by the sperm that "wins the race" and are beginning to control that factor.

But they do not also claim to control the physical and mental condition of the babies. However, over a dozen years ago, in a Czechoslovakian government clinic, Dr. Eugen Jonas claimed to do just that. Using computers, he related conception dates to the planetary patterns at the mothers' own birth dates. Apparently he achieved surprising accuracy not only in choosing boy or girl babies, but in eliminating defective infants and maternal sterility.

However, after years of seeming approval, the Communists started their cat-and-mouse game and had him institutionalized. We began corresponding with Dr. Jonas, whose work was featured in a British medical paper, some years ago. We have also had several letters from a former colleague, now in the department of psychiatry at a Canadian university. This professor tells us that Jonas was subjected to repeated harassment, then reinstatement, and that letters from him in these intervals were as lucid as before.[17] In August, 1971, he was still a practicing psychiatrist, according to a European correspondent.

Dr. Jonas's methods are much too complex to quote here in detail —but some women (he says) can conceive *only during menstruation,* and if you were born at full moon yourself, you should prevent conception at full moon. His figures showed that this opposition of sun to moon in space creates stresses which, if duplicated, can result in a defective child.

Some confirmation of Dr. Jonas's data concerning the control of the sex of babies may possibly be found in the incidence of "boy families" and "girl families." An English family, recorded since the end of the seventeenth century, produced in ten generations thirty-five children, and thirty-three of them were boys. In Nancy, France, other researchers found a "girl family" of three generations—seventy-two children, all girls.

"These families which produce exclusively male or female progeny are difficult to explain," says Rostand's *Atlas of Human Genetics*.

But it is not so well known that not only the sex, but the birth date itself, frequently recurs in family histories. Sometimes a parent or grandparents as well as three or four sons and daughters have been born on the same date in succeeding years. There are also many cases of sisters (both twins and nontwins) who give birth on the same date. This suggests that sometimes, at least, conception dates are "fixed"—as Dr. Jonas asserts.

Using more than thirty thousand birth dates, Michel Gauquelin found a hereditary tendency for children to be born under the same cosmic conditions as their parents, with the nearer bodies in the solar system in the same position. (Modern drugs, of course, may distort the rhythm by hastening the birth hour.)

When a child is born on a day of heavy magnetic disturbance, the effect is twice as strong than if he were born on a quiet day. This "shows that the planetary effect of heredity depends on the solar field. . . . But at the present time the exact nature of the physical effect and its biological mechanisms remains unknown."

Remember, Gauquelin is hostile to astrology, and Jonas uses computers (not astrologers' tables) and calls his results "cosmograms." We were surprised to find that these two men were born just seven days apart. Interested readers can find the astrological data for Gauquelin and Dr. Jonas at the end of the notes for this chapter.

12 FAMOUS TWINS—FROM MYTH TO THE PRESENT

To be born a twin in many cultures is usually fortunate. The children feel a certain distinction from their fellows and often enjoy with the birth-mate a close and lifelong companionship.

But to come into life as a twin among one of the tribes in New Guinea is a dire calamity. Among the Mundugumors of that country no child—not even a single one—is welcome. This is especially true of a male child, the rival who will soon grow up to mock his father's old age by his own virility! The husband of a pregnant wife suffers much the same taboos as a menstruating woman. There are certain things he must not touch. His mere presence works havoc with tribal magic, and if he continues to mate with his wife, he believes that he runs the horrible risk of twins.

In any case his antipregnancy magic has failed him! He may even charge his mate with adultery and will almost certainly seek another woman.

The mother-to-be thus finds her condition accursed, as it has deprived her of sex and brought the threat of a second wife. A girl child will be more welcome than a male, for she at least can be used as the purchase price to buy a wife from another tribe. In fact, if the mother is unlucky enough to have a son, she must promptly produce a sister for him for this tribal exchange!

Twin boys would almost certainly be carried to the river upon the

162

palm spathe which is used for a delivery bed and drowned, and the male half of a boy-girl twin combination would inevitably meet this fate. One of any twin pair would have to be fostered out, for the Mundugumor mother refuses to suckle two.

Apparently the majority of women in this tribe can produce milk at will. Margaret Mead writes: "Even women who have never borne children are able in a few weeks, by placing the child constantly at the breast and by drinking plenty of coconut milk, to produce enough or nearly enough milk to rear the child."

Dr. Mead discovered two sets of twins and was able to compare the one suckled thus with the child fed by its own mother and found them of equal development. Although the secretion of milk by virgins and elderly women is not unknown in medical history, some property in the coconut milk may affect it.

Yet in spite of the Mundugumors' dread of twins, it almost seems as if the tribal gods are laughing, for the ratio of twin births among them is far higher than with other New Guinea tribes.[1]

In upper Guinea twins promise fertility to the tribe and are treated with great respect. It is believed that with a single word twins can stop a boiling pot from bubbling; that they are able to predict the sex of unborn children; and that they are immune to scorpion and serpent bites. They live apart in special huts built for them by twin carpenters and observe certain taboos to protect the tribe. If one twin dies, a wooden image of him is given to the survivor and equally respected.

The Role of Twins in History

Throughout history the role of the twin has been varied and fascinating. Certain primitive Indians in southern California gave twins magnificent clothing to set them apart, but other tribes in the region feared and hated them and put them to death. They might kill the mother, too, although an occasional loving husband might sacrifice a female slave instead. If, by chance, they decided to keep the male twin, the female would be suffocated to prevent incest between them. Yet other cultures demanded that they marry after puberty. Still other tribes thought the second twin was not a real person at all, but a kind of ghost. Some tribes ruled that a man wishing to marry a twin girl must take her sister, too.

The Mohaves thought that twins came from the gods and were

clairvoyant. "We have only come to pay you a visit, our parents are 'up there'! Let us live with you a while."

The Zunis had twin war gods, Children of the Sun, who lived on remote twin peaks and controlled the outcome of all games and rivalries.

In more ancient times there were many twin gods. When born to a mortal mother with an immortal father, they were the symbols of good and evil.

Hercules, the Greek god who was given the job of cleaning out the Augean stables of the subconscious—for myths hide deep truths from the uninitiated—was a twin.

Myths also recognized the deep devotion between twins. When Castor, the mortal twin, was killed in battle, his immortal brother, Pollux, besought Jupiter to let him also die. From his throne on Mount Olympus Jupiter was stirred to pity and allowed Castor to return to earth, provided Pollux spend half the year in Hades. Later Jupiter sent them both to dwell forever in the heavens in the constellation of Gemini.

Leda and the Swan

After Leda, bathing in a stream, was ravished by Jupiter in the shape of a magnificent white swan, she was brought to bed with two eggs. From one egg came Castor and Clytemnestra, children of her husband, king of Sparta. The other egg held Jupiter's progeny, Helen and Pollux. Later, Jupiter was to father twins again when his persecuted mistress, Latona, became the mother of the twins Apollo and Diana.

These tales reveal something else. Popular opinion today supposes that the ancients were naïve or credulous, but science is learning that their so-called credulity gave them a flexibility of mind that led to many insights. Their myths prove they knew that more than one father is possible with both human and animal multiples. Yet it is only quite recently as time goes that modern man has been forced to admit this fact through blood tests in court.

Even primitive Brazilian Indians had twin gods of such power that they caused the Flood. And they, too, were sons of different fathers— a mortal and a god. But twins were abnormal, and so with most primitives they had to be an evil omen. To them man's chief distinction from animals was single births, and multiples seemed nonhuman and bestial.

Although multiple births among apes are very uncommon, the Dahomeys believed that without a proper ceremony by the witch doctor, twins could become monkeys again. Perhaps most of their fear came from their belief that man could not father more than one child at a time—hence the wife must have been unfaithful and could blast the crops if she worked in the fields. To appease the devils, she and the twins might both be sacrificed.

Theodore Roosevelt wrote to Dr. Newman that when he asked why they killed twins in northern Luzon, the Igorot women told him, "We do not wish to be like a dog, and have litters."

He also described a police corporal, a twin who had been placed in a jar and left to die. His brother, however, died first, so they hastily retrieved him from the jar. Roosevelt went on to say that in the backcountry of China one twin was believed to be an evil spirit trying to get a foothold on earth, and they called in the witch doctor to determine the evil twin.

The same practice prevails among certain African tribes. Twins come from two fathers, one of them a wizard who has his eye on the woman. When she becomes pregnant by her husband, the wizard then has intercourse with her in her sleep. (That's how baby wizards are born!) A clever witch doctor can find out "through the bones" which is the human child. But if no medicine man is handy, the midwife strangles both babies rather than risk having a baby wizard survive.

According to *Ebony* magazine, "As recently as 1946 a special orphanage for twins was required in southern Rhodesia because the natives habitually abandoned them, doubting they could have the same father."[2]

Twins among Primitive Tribes

In southeast Africa the Barongas believe twins control the weather. Their mother will be renamed Tilo, the Sky, and the twins known as Children of the Sky. When crops are scorched and the rains won't come, the women perform obscene dances.

They then go to the sacred groves to pour water on the graves, especially the graves of twins. Twins' graves, they believe, must always be kept moist and are usually near a lake. If the rains still hold off, someone may remember that a certain twin was buried in a dry spot, and then they know why the sky continues fiery. The bones are dug up, the twin is replanted, and now the rains are sure to come!

A powerful cult of the twins exists in the voodoo religion in Haiti. Whether living or dead, they are exceptional beings, invoked and saluted at the beginning of rituals. "Sometimes a family reeling under a series of misfortunes learns from a *hungan* (priest) that it has been neglecting twins far back in its ancestry" and reparation must be made.

A Haitian child with webbed feet is a twin that has "eaten" its brother in the womb. The spirits of dead twins are worshiped and feared, for they are very touchy and if not given food at feasts, may obsess the living. Even living twins are given solicitous attention, for they can call down wrath on their parents.

Consequently twins become tyrants from childhood. They usually hate each other and have to be constantly watched, treated exactly alike, and their plates switched about at meals to keep them harmonized by eating each other's food. Clothes must be identical, and girl twins must be married close together. When a woman with a twin brother marries, he is showered with gifts to prevent resentment.

If one twin dies, the other still sets aside food and gifts for him. The ancestral twins are prayed to for the sick and are believed to cause dreams revealing the proper remedies. Some believe all twins share the same soul.[3]

Among those South American tribes who value twins, some believe it possible to "make" twins by sympathetic magic. If a woman eats two bananas growing from a single head, she can achieve this distinction; or a double grain of millet can do it.

Sir James G. Frazer, author of *The Golden Bough,* says the belief in twins' great power over nature is very widespread. The Tsimshian Indians of British Columbia pray to the wind and rain, "Calm down, breath of the twins!" They also think twins invariably have their wishes granted, and fear twins' power to injure anyone they hate. Since they can "call the salmon," the Tsimshian word for twin means "making plentiful." Some of the other Indians of British Columbia believe twins were magically changed from salmon to children; hence they forbid them to go near any water for fear they might be transformed back into fish.

Jacob and Esau

One of the oldest stories of twins that we have goes back to the first book of the Old Testament, Genesis—the tale of the crafty mother and son, Rebekah and Jacob, who plotted against his brother Esau. Because of the differing descriptions of the two boys, they were obviously fraternal, not identical, twins.

Isaac was forty when he took Rebekah to wife, and for twenty years she remained barren. Then he entreated the Lord, and she conceived twins. Feeling the children struggling so vigorously in her womb, Rebekah was puzzled, "and she went to inquire of the Lord. And the Lord said unto her, two nations are in thy womb . . . and the older shall serve the younger."

And when her days were fulfilled, behold, the first came out red all over like a hairy garment, and they called him Esau ("Hairy"). And after that his brother came out, his hand holding Esau's heel, so they named him Jacob ("Heel-catcher").

Esau grew to be a cunning hunter, beloved of his father for the tasty venison he brought home, while Jacob was Rebekah's favorite. When Isaac was old and his eyes were dim, he sent for his favorite and begged him to take his bow and arrow and go out after a deer.

"And make me a savoury meat such as I love . . . that my soul may bless thee before I die."

But the trickster Rebekah was listening, and when Esau had gone, she sent for Jacob. He must go quickly to kill two kids, and she would make a stew for him so that he could get the blessing in Esau's place.

"But my brother Esau is a hairy man," Jacob objected. "My father may feel me, and I will receive his curse instead of his blessing!"

But Rebekah was quite equal to this. She put the skins of the kids over his hands and the back of his neck and dressed him in Esau's raiment, which smelt of the woods. And when Isaac asked how he had killed a deer so quickly, Jacob did not hesitate to say that the Lord had sent it to him!

But Isaac was suspicious. "Come near that I may feel thee, my son!" And he put his hands on the kids' hairy skin. "The voice is Jacob's," the senile old man said in bewilderment, "but the hands are the hands of Esau." But doddering and weary unto death, he gave to Jacob the blessing that belonged to the firstborn.

Scarcely had Jacob left the tent when Esau appeared with the real venison stew. And Isaac trembled in dismay. "Thy brother hath tricked me! I have blessed him instead—yea, and he shall be blessed!" (A blessing, once given, could not be canceled.) "Behold, I have made him thy Lord, and what shall I now do unto thee, my son?"

And Esau lifted up his voice and wept. So he hated his brother, whom Rebekah quickly sent to safety to an uncle. And it came to pass, as the Lord had told her before the twins were born, that the elder served the younger, and Esau lost his birthright.

Other Famous Twins

Possibly the most famous of all twins in the Christian world is one of the Apostles, St. Thomas. His twin is unknown to history, but we know that one existed, for he is referred to in Scripture as "Thomas, called Didymus," the Greek word for twin. In fact, Thomas itself means twin in Aramaic.

Anthony and Cleopatra also had twins—Alexander Helios and Cleopatra Selene. When the twins were four years old, Anthony married Cleopatra, although he was still married to Octavia, his fourth wife. After Cleopatra's stunt with the asp, the long-suffering Octavia took in Cleopatra's three children by Anthony and eventually married off Cleo-Selene to Juba, king of Numidia. What happened to the boy twin is not told.

Parish records show that Shakespeare was the father of twins, Hamnet and Judith. They were baptized on February 2, 1585. Shortly before her famous father's death, Judith married a wine merchant of Stratford-on-Avon named Thomas Quincy, and their three sons all died unmarried. Judith's twin brother, Hamnet, succumbed at the age of eleven.

However, considering the number of twins through the centuries, the proportion of famous ones is very small. The father and uncle of the great Johann Sebastian Bach, who were also musicians, were twins. So were F. R. and F. O. Stanley, inventors of the old Stanley Steamer automobile; also Jean and Auguste Piccard, stratosphere balloonists and scientists. Jean's balloon ascents and Auguste's interest in the ocean depths brought them the titles "Mr. Up" and "Mr. Down."

When Dr. Newman was winning a name as a twin expert at the University of Chicago back in the 1930's, Jean Piccard was also a member of the faculty. Because both men were twins, they often discussed twinship and agreed that scientists needed more marriages between one-egg twins to pin things down.

Apparently Jean took this to heart and decided to become a guinea pig, for some years later he married a one-egg twin. Still later he brought his own twin, Auguste, to meet Newman—who was interested to see that Jean was right-handed, with a clockwise hair whorl, and Auguste was his opposite, or mirror-image.

Jean told him the results of his own "experiment" in marriage to another one-egg twin. He had had three sons, single births but showing some evidence of having begun as twins. With the first boy a *fetus papyraceous* (the mummified remains of a twin brother) was attached to the living twin's placenta. The second son's placenta had a large cyst containing tissues thought to be the remains of a twin embryo. With the third son the only such suggestion, which is not necessarily proof, was that there was some evidence of reverse-image in his own body.

A tale of ingenious twin mischief is told of the Piccards. Jean and Auguste decided they would have a bit of fun with a barber near their home in Switzerland. When Jean went in for a shave, he complained that he had a most annoying beard—so heavy that he had to shave several times a day.

The barber was challenged to the quick. This could *never* happen with his trusty razor! When Jean said that no barber had been able to prevent it before, the angry man offered him a free shave if he needed one before twenty-four hours. Jean let him scrape away—and several hours later sent Auguste in with a heavy stubble. He collected his free shave and left a stunned barber pondering on the most amazing beard of his career.

Psychologists suggest that because twins are apt to make a happy, extroverted adjustment to life, they have less need to compete for the world's acclaim. If they do win fame together, it is apt to be in sports or in show business, where twinship brings quick publicity and the fame is likely to be short-lived.

The famous author Thornton Wilder is a twin. In his well-known novel *The Bridge of San Luis Rey* he explores some twists of twinship. His characters, Manuel and Esteban, are ashamed of being twins and "suffer . . . in stolid patience." Yet when Esteban loses his twin in death, he falls into a frenzy, calling himself Manuel and crying, "I am alone, alone, alone!"

Two other writers, in the newspaper field, Ann Landers and Abigail Van Buren, became rivals when both became advice columnists. The twins were born in Sioux City, Iowa, and undoubtedly got their remarkable verve and love of people from their father. A Russian immigrant, he rose from selling poultry from a wagon to ownership of a three-state theatre chain.

No one could tell one twin from the other at first. Named Esther Pauline and Pauline Esther (nicknamed Eppie and Popo), they were inseparable, dressing and even thinking alike clear up to a double wedding. But when Eppie landed the Ann Landers column with the Chicago *Sun Times* in a competition, Popo went her one better as her own boss with the brand-new "Dear Abby" column for the San Francisco *Chronicle*.

For a time they avoided each other. It did not help the armed truce when *Time* reported that Ann called Abby "very imitative," and Abby replied: "Blood is thicker than water—and it boils quicker." Their basic likeness is obvious in their replies to the troubled.

The wound soon healed, and in March, 1971, Abby wrote us:

> We are very good friends now, and have been for nearly five years. We celebrate our birthdays (July 4) and wedding anniversaries (July 2) together, since we were married at a double wedding. Every July the two of us and our great, great husbands take a fun trip to some outlandish place . . . like Iran (last year) . . . and this year we plan to go to Yugoslavia and Vienna.
>
> She is really a fantastic girl and we do love each other very much. This world is plenty big enough for her success and my own. We have both been so lucky in our professional lives as well as in our personal lives that our cup runneth over.

Long and happily married today, both women have incomes in six figures. Both need a staff of secretaries to sort mail and type, but they write their own replies, and even on planes and under the hair drier they answer the daily mountain of mail. Both have been known to reply by telegram and have contacts with many agencies across the nation to whom they direct correspondents in deep trouble. Their WATS telephone lines cost $24,000 a year and permit unlimited cross-country calls.

In their columns they are famous for the verbal kick in the pants.[4] Neither tolerates two-timing, impudence to parents, or lack of chastity. Abby has no sympathy for braggarts. Asked by a handsome male how to drive off his horde of admirers, she advised, "Keep talking!" Mini-mothers need the courage to say no and stick to it. "Woe to the girl who is being coached from the sidelines by a mother who never made the team!"

Her twin Ann's answer to Want-to-Tell-Her-Off is a classic: "Pass up the inclination. Samson slew a thousand men with the jawbone of an ass. Every day thousands more slay themselves with the same weapon. Don't be among them!"

She has equally pungent comments on parental attitudes: "What the vast majority of American children needs is to stop being pampered, stop being indulged, stop being chauffered, gifted, catered to, and made to feel the world belongs to them and they are doing their parents a big favor by letting them live in it."

A nonfiction best-seller, also written by twins and brought up to date every year or two, is the *Guinness Book of World Records*. Seemingly the authors, Norris and Ross McWhirter, emerged from the cradle asking questions and have never stopped since. So they were naturals for the job when the famous makers of Guinness beer and stout wanted a book to settle the sort of arguments that spring up in English pubs. Such questions as which is the biggest, the oldest, the heaviest, of an inconceivable variety of persons and things are answered here. Some of the facts in our book come from their compilation. If you enjoy arguments about facts, theirs is a useful volume to own.

Another pair of "twins"—Loren and Lorene—had brief fame during a 1922 murder trial in Hammond, Indiana.

All his life Frank McNally had longed for children of his own. When he was sixty-nine, his young wife, twenty-three, made him deliriously happy with the announcement that a baby was on the way.

Soon after, with only the help of a woman friend who lived with them, Hazel gave birth to twins in their home. But Frank was not permitted to see his offspring. Loren and Lorene were very sickly and must not be subjected to any stray germs! All she allowed Frank to do was to stand outside her room and listen to the babies' occasional crying spells.

For a year McNally put up with this. Then his wife suddenly declared they were critically ill and rushed them to Chicago while he was out of the house. A week later she was back—minus the twins. They had died and been buried in the big city! This was too thick even for the long-suffering Frank. Enraged, he had her accused and tried for murder.

But Hazel was acquitted. Her lawyer proved in court that she was incapable of bearing a child and had invented the fantasy to please Frank. When the deception became too involved, she decided upon the fake burial. To clinch it, her lawyer unwrapped a large box and drew out "Loren and Lorene"—two large crying dolls![5]

13 AMAZING DOUBLES—
NONTWINS

The story of twins would hardly be complete without a chapter on "doubles"—those mysterious nontwins who occasionally appear, causing endless confusion and sometimes sorrow.

Are we born in schools like fish, with certain affinities among us, certain likenesses between one individual who happened to be born in the South and another in the North or between one in America and one in Europe?

In an earlier chapter we inquired further into this mystery, but here we deal only with physical doubles. It may be pertinent, however, to quote Sir William Osler, the noted professor of medicine at Oxford: "No human being is constituted to know the truth, the whole truth, and nothing but the truth; and even the best of men must be content with fragments, with partial glimpses, never the full fruition."

Double Trouble

We cannot strip life of the mysterious by even the most minute inspection of specimens impaled on pins like butterflies in a glass case. However, for your inspection, here are a few butterflies. When you finish, you may wonder if you, too, have a double somewhere—and probably you'll devoutly hope that you do not.

The notorious John Dillinger had a double named Ralph Alsman.

Forced by his occupation to travel through Dillinger's territory in the Midwest, Alsman always informed the police before his arrival and constantly carried detailed identification during the final search for the gangster. Only Dillinger's death dispelled the constant shadow of arrest that hung over his innocent double's life. But other doubles have not been so fortunate.

The Adam Weaver Case

Sheriff Metas Atherholt expected trouble as he climbed isolated Haycock Mountain in Bucks County, Pennsylvania, to arrest Adam Weaver. Cautiously he approached the cabin with his deputy, hoping to catch the burly mountaineer by surprise in the dusk.

When the sheriff knocked on the door, it swung open. Weaver was seated at a table at one end of the shack, his wife beside a stove at the opposite end. Weaver looked up, startled, then he glanced at his shotgun in a corner nearby.

"The storekeeper at Bursonville claims you stole some food and cartridges from him, Weaver," the sheriff said. "I'm placing you under arrest."

"He's a liar!" cried Weaver.

With a quick movement of his arm he knocked the oil lamp from the table. As the two officers drew their revolvers, Weaver's wife flung a kettle of boiling water at them. They stumbled, blinded by the scalding liquid. At the same instant, the shotgun roared twice, and the cabin door slammed shut.

Wounded in the shoulder, Sheriff Atherholt wiped his eyes dry and looked around him. Weaver had fled. Mrs. Weaver was lighting another oil lamp and sobbing. On the floor lay the deputy—dead.

Posses searched in all directions, but they failed to find any trace of the fugitive. In due time Mrs. Weaver was convicted of complicity in the murder and sent to prison. Her five children were claimed by distant relatives. The shack was left deserted.

Adam Weaver had been a man of unusual appearance, with red hair and a stubby red beard. Grim and taciturn, with a violent temper, he had long been feared and hated by his neighbors.

Now he became a legend. "Adam will return," Mrs. Weaver had said at her trial. "Someday he will come back."

But years passed as the abandoned cabin slowly fell into ruins. Two decades later, one afternoon in 1922, Sheriff Harry Rhodes,

Atherholt's successor, noticed a stranger near the cabin gathering twigs. The man was dressed in shabby garments and had red hair and a sandy beard. When the officer ordered him to move along, the man silently picked up a bundle and walked away.

But when the sheriff told some of the older residents about the stranger, a flood of questions followed. The man was about sixty— Weaver's age if he were still alive—and his general appearance was the same. Among the old records at the jail, the sheriff found a yellowed photograph of the long-missing murderer.

There could be little doubt about it! Adam Weaver had come home at last!

The following day, the officer found the man at the shack again and arrested him for vagrancy. Without protest the man accompanied the sheriff back down the mountain road.

"What's your name?" the sheriff inquired.

"Haycocks. Roy Haycocks."

"But that's the name of this mountain here!" the officer said, surprised.

"Curious coincidence, isn't it?" was the stranger's comment.

Taken to the jail at Doylestown, the man refused to talk. The old photograph revealed only those changes that twenty years would create. Weaver had been of Pennsylvania German stock. The stranger spoke with a slight German accent, but insisted he couldn't speak the language. Weaver had been known to have a small scar on his chin, but the suspect angrily refused to be shaved.

"I've worn that beard for eight years," he said. "My religion won't let me shave it off."

Three old residents positively identified the stranger as the missing outlaw. Mrs. Weaver, now demented, was confined in a state asylum, and Sheriff Atherholt was dead.

But Sheriff Rhodes wanted positive proof of identification. He gave a picture of the suspect to a national press service. Meanwhile, one of Weaver's sons was located in Philadelphia and brought to Doylestown along with a brother-in-law of the fugitive. When they stood face to face, no sign of recognition was displayed by the older man, but the son nodded his head. "You are my father!" he asserted.

"Never saw you before," the prisoner replied.

"That's a lie! You bullied me when I was a kid. You drove my mother insane. You're my father!"

"Nonsense! I don't know who you are or what you're talking

about. Never had a family. I came east from Illinois ten years ago and been minding my own business ever since."

Now the brother-in-law turned to the sheriff. "This man is Adam Weaver, Officer," he said. "I'm sure of it."

"My name is Haycocks," the suspect insisted. "H-e-c-o-x." The spelling didn't agree with his pronunciation.

The sheriff ignored his remark. "Adam Weaver," he said, "you returned to your old cabin. You have been positively identified by five persons, one of them your own son. I am filing a charge of murder against you."

The next morning another man arrived in Doylestown. He went to the jail and asked to see the suspect. When the prisoner was brought from his cell, the visitor smiled. "Well, Roy," he said, "I've come to take you home."

"All right," the prisoner answered. "I'll come."

The man turned to the sheriff. "This is my brother, Roy Hecox. Ten years ago we lived at Homer, Illinois. Then my mother and I moved to California, and Roy came east. Guess he's been a vagabond ever since, but he's not the kind of a man who makes trouble. He just has his own ideas about living."

Sheriff Rhodes, startled, asked: "You can prove this?"

"Of course." He removed a bulky envelope of papers and pictures from his pocket. "My mother noticed a picture of Roy in a Santa Barbara newspaper and read the story that he was suspected of being a murderer named Weaver. She asked me to come and clear him, and here I am. Roy is harmless, I assure you."

When the two brothers left the jail and walked to the railroad station, a crowd of curious citizens followed. Out from under the shadow of the gallows, Roy enjoyed all the attention he received. Saved by the chance publication of a picture in a newspaper thousands of miles away, he went back to California to spend his remaining years on his brother's ranch in peace.

As for Adam Weaver—no man knows.

The Tiger Girl

In the twenties and thirties the Bonnie-and-Clyde type of couple were common in the West Virginia and Pennsylvania hills. During the fall of 1929 one of these pairs began holding up filling stations and restaurants. The man was tall, thin, and handsome; his "moll" was a thickset blonde who called herself the Tiger Girl and always wore a black satin turban with a flashy rhinestone pin in front. They traveled in a black touring car.

One September night they held up a service station near Mounds-ville, West Virginia, operated by an elderly man named Cott. He told the sheriff they looked familiar to him, and he thought that later on he'd remember where he had seen them.

Two weeks later he telephoned the lawman. "I know who those crooks are now," he announced excitedly. "They live near here—about twenty miles out. Frank and Norma Howell!"

It happened that the Howells were known to Chief of Police John Arnette, so he took over from the sheriff. Howell was a quiet country fellow who performed odd jobs as well as hunting and fishing to support his wife and three children. Mrs. Howell, a chunky, good-looking blonde, had recently bought herself a black turban with a gaudy rhinestone pin. Like many mountain women, she was a crack shot.

Chief Arnette was struck by these facts and how well they matched the description of the busy bandits. The Howells couldn't prove where they were on the night Cott was robbed, but insisted they had been at home. There wasn't money enough to go out much.

"Your landlord tells me that you were behind in your rent but paid it all up two days after Old Man Cott was robbed," the chief said. "How come?"

"I already had the rent money," Howell replied. "I just didn't get around to paying it on time."

"I know you have a black touring car. How come you could buy it?"

"It took a while, but I saved the money."

The chief examined the car and discovered its engine had been souped up. Howell explained that he liked to tinker with cars.

At headquarters Cott positively identified the couple. Frank went on trial first. His only witnesses were his three children—the eldest thirteen—who testified he had been home the night of the holdup. Frank was sentenced to fifteen years in the penitentiary. When Norma went on trial, the jury believed the children, and she was acquitted. As if she were jinxed, almost immediately someone in

Cadiz, Ohio, identified her as the bandit in another holdup, but a second jury freed her.

Now she set to work desperately to free her husband. But she had no money, and lawyers weren't interested. To support her children and herself she did cleaning and washings. Each night she carefully read the local newspaper.

Months went by. Finally she spotted a news story about a pair of bandits caught in Arizona. One was a tall, slender man; the other a stocky blonde who was wearing a black turban with a pin. They were wanted for the holdup murder of a storekeeper in a Pennsylvania town near the West Virginia border. She hurried to Chief Arnette and begged him to check it out.

"I can't waste my time that way," he said. "Cott identified your husband, and a jury convicted him. Be glad for your children's sake that you got off yourself!"

The bandit pair, Glenn Dague and Irene Schroeder, were brought to trial, sentenced to die in the electric chair, and taken to the state prison at Bellefontaine. They had less than two months to live when Norma thought of writing a letter to Irene Schroeder asking if she and Dague had committed the Cott robbery. "My husband is in prison for this holdup," she wrote. "You are mountain folk same as us. I know you'll do the right thing by me."

To her joy Irene wrote back from the death house. Yes, they were guilty. "Glenn and I will do anything we can to free your husband. We have nothing to lose now, and we don't want anybody going to prison for something we've done."

But when Norma took the letter to Chief Arnette, he obstinately refused to believe it. "That dame is making a grandstand play, hoping to get a reprieve! Cott identified Frank, and we have only her word that she did it. The law has been carried out."

Norma left his office weeping.

She tried to see Lloyd Arnold, the county prosecutor, but he was away on a long vacation. The execution was only three weeks off. Desperately she went to the service station, but Cott only shrugged when she begged him to go to the prison.

"I got a business to run and no time for a wild-goose chase," he insisted. "I know who held me up. It was you and that husband of yours. Now beat it!"

In despair Norma wrote Irene again. "Can you think of anything to prove it was you?" she asked. "Some bit of evidence?"

Irene answered, saying that Cott had a severe cold that night and was sneezing and blowing his nose. "He ought to remember that!"

Norma took the letter to Cott. "I think you told her to write that so you could spring your husband" was his reply. "You've cheated the law once, and you're trying to do it again. If you show up here again, I'm going to have you arrested. Now beat it!"

Just ten days before the execution, Prosecutor Arnold returned from his vacation. Norma was waiting in his office. This time the plucky woman got action.

"I've never had a case of mistaken identity," he said, "but they do happen. I'll check it out."

The next day they called on Cott. At first he refused to go to the prison.

"You have little choice," Arnold pointed out. "The case hinges on your identification."

When they entered the death house and Irene appeared wearing her black turban and pin, Cott's mouth fell open. He turned to Arnold. "God, but I'm sorry. I made a mistake. This is the woman who held me up." He looked at Norma. "I did what I thought was right. I hope you'll forgive me." Moments later he identified Dague as the guilty man.

Snow was falling that night in February, 1931, when Norma Howell heard over the radio that Irene Schroeder and Glenn Dague had just been executed. "Thank you, God! Thank you, Irene!" she whispered, her eyes filled with tears.

All arrangements had been completed. Frank was coming home.

More Experiences with Doubles

In March, 1966, Jack Moffitt, in his column "The Cracker Barrel" in the Los Angeles *Herald Examiner,* ran a notice that we were looking for cases of people who knew they had almost exact doubles:

> I can give the Gaddises a couple of personal instances. In 1953, when I was working for our State Department in Munich, Germany, several friends sent me postal cards showing the lobby of a hotel in Helsinki, Finland. Seated in the foreground was a man who was an exact double of myself. I've never been in Helsinki.
>
> An even stranger, twin-like experience occurred to me on a January day in 1928 in a barber shop in Granada, Spain. I was despairing of making my wishes known to any of the barbers when a familiar voice

addressed me in English. It was the exact voice of a friend, Conrad Carlson, who was a reporter on the Kansas City *Star*. I turned to face a man whose appearance was an exact duplicate of Carlson's rugged Lincoln-like face and figure. He even duplicated a slight cast Carlson had in one eye. After the stranger had kindly translated my needs to the barber, I told him of the startling resemblance. He was a pure-blood Spaniard while Carlson was a Swedish American. At that time, neither man had ever been outside his native country.

Following this notice in Moffitt's column, we received several letters from readers giving their experiences with doubles. The most interesting came from Mr. L. S. Cusick, of Woodland Hills, California:

I had just such an encounter [as Jack Moffitt's] while in Europe after World War II in a unit waiting to be shipped home and discharged. Men from all over the European Theater were transferred into a division that was designated to accept all men from many different divisions . . . prior to returning home on a full ship. I can't even recall the particular division except the shoulder patch was a small hatchet stuck in a log—I think they referred to it as the Railsplitters. At any rate I was from the 78th Infantry Division.

We were all assembling outside the town of Heidelberg, and I first became aware of my double in the chow line one morning. It occurred to me that my double looked familiar—not that I thought he looked like me, really. A couple of my friends even asked if the fellow was my twin brother—which, of course, finally led us to talking to each other—and then we realized *why* we didn't exactly recognize ourselves. It was because every morning we looked at our own mirror image, so this is how we came to recognize ourselves in our minds. When we then had an opportunity to compare photos, the exact likeness was at once obvious.

From then on we had a great time telling everyone we were twins, making up wild stories about our being separated by the Army, etc. On the boat home I took some photos of my double with a friend of mine, and some with myself and the same friend. Even my mother and father could not tell the difference, and only by knowing how I had posed my double was I really sure myself.

He couldn't recall the man's name or birthplace, but he did remember that they were both born under the sign of Aquarius.

Doubles of Famous Men

Sometimes people who happen to dislike famous men take delight in capitalizing on their chance likeness. This happened to William Gladstone, Prime Minister of England in Queen Victoria's day. He had a double who found mischievous pleasure in making enemies for Gladstone. This individual, after rudely repelling the advances of strangers on the street, would chuckle, "Well, I trust I have deprived Mr. Gladstone of one more admirer!"

And David Lloyd George, Britain's fiery Welsh Prime Minister during World War I, was plagued in the same manner by a double who deliberately created all kinds of confusion.

It was also reported that Stalin had five doubles who were made up like him for security reasons. Churchill was similarly protected. One of the actors who played his part was so like him that "Winnie" himself, shown an old documentary film using this man, swore it must have been himself.

Autoscopic Hallucinations

Still other "double" cases are those not seen by other people, but by the individual himself. These medical or psychological phenomena have been known for centuries and today are termed autoscopic hallucinations.

Dr. N. Lukianowicz, of Barrow Hospital, in Bristol, England, discussed the subject in the *Archives of Neurology and Psychiatry,* published by the American Medical Association. He described various cases of patients having seen themselves as phantoms coming toward them.[1]

In one example Mrs. Anna W. of London, England, returning from her husband's funeral in 1956, saw a strange woman in mourning walking in front of her. When she undressed at home in a well-lighted room, the other woman did the same. Then, with a chill of fright, she saw it was her own face looking back at her. Later she said that it was seemingly more warm and alive than herself. It vanished when she lay down but returned very briefly several times.

A Chicago man, Harold C., who suffered from frequent migraine headaches, began having these hallucinations. He might see his own double sitting opposite him at a table for periods of up to an hour or on the golf course and other places. But the phenomenon occurred only after a migraine attack.

Sometimes such visions are associated with epilepsy. Manuel K., of New York City, had suffered these seizures for several years. In April, 1959, he visited a friend in a hospital. As he sat down beside the bed, a chill crept over him. There exactly opposite him on the other side of his friend's bed and duplicating his every movement was a double of himself. Observing that no one else noticed it, he made no reference to it. Sometime later the vision repeated itself while he was typing a letter, and he observed his image making the same movements.

On very rare occasions these images have been heard (by the victim) to speak. In one possibly unique case a woman applying her makeup saw her image doing the same thing. She reached out to touch her double and to her abject horror felt herself being touched on her face in return. A startling tactile hallucination!

Dr. Lukianowicz said there are two theories as to the origin of autoscopic hallucinations: first, some irritating process in the brain or, second, the projection of a memory picture. How an image that duplicates the actions of the observer at the precise instant of the vision can be a "memory picture" is not explained.

These images, however, do not always duplicate the hallucinator's actions. Instead they may be attempts at wish fulfillment, as when a man playing classical phonograph records looked up and saw his double conducting an orchestra that was playing the same music. Others have reported their doubles doing things they have always wished to do, such as pitching ball, piloting a plane, etc. Probably the two types are different in origin, the latter being an actual hallucination and the former a vision depending on a freak situation—possibly some trick of body chemistry or stimulation of the macrophage system. The usually brief vision is in colorless grays.

Abraham Lincoln had such an experience. We take the story from Dr. Werner Wolff's book on handwriting and personality, *Diagrams of the Unconscious,* in which he quotes William H. Herndon, Lincoln's friend and law associate for twenty-five years.

In a letter dated July 17, 1887, Herndon wrote: "He [Lincoln] was a man of opposites, of terrible contrasts"—one day one man, the next, another. On another occasion Herndon said Lincoln was "a peculiar mysterious man . . . a double consciousness, a double life. The two states, never in a normal man, co-exist in equal and vigorous activities, though they succeed each other quickly."

And Dr. Wolff wrote: "Lincoln himself had this feeling of a dual personality, which became manifest for him in strange sensations of split personality." Emil Ludwig in his biography of Lincoln quotes Lincoln's own account of an experience that he gave a friend:

> Once, after a tumultuous and tiring day, I threw myself down on an old sofa at home. Opposite where I lay was a bureau with a swinging glass upon it, and looking in that glass, I saw myself reflected nearly at full length; but my face, I noticed, had two separate and distinct images, the tip of the nose of one being about three inches from the tip of the other.
>
> I was a little bothered, perhaps startled, and got up and looked in the glass, but the illusion vanished. On lying down again, I saw it a second time, plainer, if possible, than before; and then I noticed that one of the faces was a little paler—say, five shades—than the other. I got up, and the thing melted away, and I went off, and in the excitement of the hour forgot all about it—nearly, but not quite, for the thing would once in a while come up, and give me a little pang, as if something uncomfortable had happened.

Remembering what a tall, gaunt man Lincoln was causes us to speculate: Could Lincoln have been one of those cases of the extra Y chromosome that occurs among athletes and unusual, brilliant personalities as well as among criminals? We will, of course, never know.

14 THE CLUBS "WHERE GOD CHOOSES THE MEMBERS"

For several years I (the feminine half of this writing team) was an honorary member of a local Mothers of Twins Club. I was introduced to it through its founder, Shirley Niehoff, whose experience with triplets begins our chapter on the trips, quads, and quints. Although merely the mother of a singleton myself, I found the meetings fascinating, and obviously they were a lifeline to the mothers.

"I'd been ready to flip," Shirley said. "It was hard enough to handle the two boys—and here were three more new babies! Yelling, soaked, and hungry—usually at the same time, day and night!"

By this time her husband had been transferred to Miramar Naval Base in San Diego, and they were living among strangers in a smaller town nearby. Lonesome, exhausted, and unhappy, she was sure there must be others in the same boat. She had heard of the Mothers of Twins Clubs elsewhere. Why not start one?

So she and another potential MOT got busy. In a very short time, through the hospital, doctors, and a notice in the paper, they rounded up twenty women. The newcomers were just as eager for togetherness as they, and soon each hostess's living room was crowded to capacity at the monthly meetings.

From girls still in their teens to women with "menopause twins," each had knowledge and experience to contribute to the varied problems involved in rearing twins and supertwins. One thing stands out about the mothers of multiples—enthusiasm and pride in self and offspring. Since nature has set them apart, they want to do the job right.

Sharing Experiences and Economics

Learning painfully from hindsight, they have distilled their own multiple-wisdom by discussing countless emergencies and attitudes that singletons do not present. Not the least of the benefits is having someone as close as the telephone in a crisis—especially here where many of the girls are navy wives with husbands at sea. Some are under twenty, separated from home for the first time and terrified by the idea of twins. Friendships like these provide a dozen fairy god-mothers, and their "hot line" ringing at 5 A.M. may be a desperate cry for help.

One girl told a family legend of seven-months twins saved many years ago in a Catholic hospital during a Minnesota blizzard. The nuns popped the preemies into shoe boxes and rushed them to the convent kitchen. There they slept night after night beside the open door of a wood-burning range with a nun nodding beside them until all danger was past. However, I could not authenticate this tale.

MOTs share many small economies, such as using mineral oil and a big shaker full of cornstarch instead of baby oil and powder. In addition to such expertise, they reduce the staggering costs of mul-tiples through their Exchange Bank of outgrown baby (and maternity) clothes, strollers, cribs, and equipment, and work out a point system of baby-sitting among themselves.

After the Niehoff triplets consumed forty dollars' worth of canned food in their first month, Shirley bought the sturdiest blender she could find. Then it was easy to liquidize some of the vegetables and fruits (and later, meats) while she prepared her meals. She did this before seasoning, since there is evidence that salt can be harmful to babies, especially if a family tendency to high blood pressure exists. (Canned baby foods and cereals are salted to appeal to the mother's taste.) Cooked cereals also smooth down in a jiffy. All these foods can be frozen in small plastic bags in ice-cube trays, then quickly warmed in a bowl of hot water.

The Subject of Breast-Feeding

Several MOTs were enthusiasts when the topic of breast-feeding twins arose. "It's the biggest labor-saving device on the market, and just about the only easy, simple, and cheap by-product of producing twins!" they insisted. They got their figures back faster (multiples stretch the uterus more) and had much more rest. Instead of the exhausting routine of formulas, bottles, and chilly nighttime feedings, they take the babies to bed and often delay weaning by supplementing with bottles and nursing one baby a day.

"But can I ever do it?" asked a pregnant member. "My sister tried and gave up."

"I read that it depends on your attitude toward sex," another contributed. "If you think sex is a nuisance, the milk stops!"

Everyone doubted the validity of this remark, so one of the older mothers who had breast-fed all of her six children, including her menopause twins, offered to research breast versus bottle. Later, her club program, voted the best in months, produced an imposing array of facts.

Some came from Dr. Niles Newton (herself both the mother of four and a professor of psychology at Northwestern University Medical School) and her husband, Dr. Michael Newton.[1] Other sources included the La Leche (Lay-chay) League International, 9616 Minneapolis Avenue, Franklin Park, Illinois 60131.

La Leche ("The Milk"), established only in 1956, now has local clubs throughout the United States led by experienced mothers eager to help and an advisory board of thirty-five physicians. Members even volunteer surplus milk to be shipped frozen to sickly babies. Human milk has two to three times as much vitamin C as cow's milk, and twenty times as much vitamin E (unless the mother is deficient, which is often the case with premature babies—and possibly a cause). It also has half again as much lactose and less ash and casein. The league sells a comprehensive manual, *The Womanly Art of Breast Feeding*.

Many researchers now believe that cow's milk is the trigger that sets off such allergies in babies as rashes, indigestion, hay fever, and asthma. In a Chicago study twenty thousand infants were checked through the first year of life. Bottle-fed babies had twice as many infections, and ten times more died from them. Human milk contains antibodies against human ailments and aids brain development. If breast-feeding is impossible, soy-bean milk or other noncow's milk may help. But the nipple designed by Goodyear, not by God, is a far-from-perfect substitute.[2]

Also, the rate of breast cancer is far lower among women who have nursed their babies, and there are other rewards. "I simply cannot describe what breast-feeding did for our family," our MOT read from her notes to us. "I became a truly happy person for the first time in my life, my marriage is close, and I can *love* my husband and children as I never knew how before."

And yes, our researcher asserted, it really is true that a woman's ability to nurse is tied to her attitudes, especially toward sex. "Women who prefer to bottle-feed," she went on, "have more psychosexual disturbances. . . . If they really *want* to breast-feed, they can produce enough milk!

"If the modern mother could spend more time baring her breast to the mouth of her baby, she would spend less time baring the details of her troubled emotional life to the doctor or bewailing the poor health of her children."[3]

Mothers of first babies who plan to nurse even seem to have shorter labor and their infants gain faster. But since drugs given the mother often damage the child's ability to suck for several days, don't give up too soon! Also, two babies stimulate twice as much milk. One mother whose baby didn't even come home from the hospital for eight weeks was able to nurse through persistent effort, then continued for an entire year.[4] (Remember the Mundugumor savages, where *women who had never borne a child* could still wet-nurse a twin after patient attempts?)

"When you see your twins' little hands and feet moving rhythmically like a kitten nursing, you know you're giving them something more precious than milk. So girls, don't sell yourselves short and add to the woes with formulas and frenzy!" our MOT concluded her paper.

MOTs learn that it helps the children's development to trade one twin back and forth among themselves for a few hours. Separate your pairs, and let one child play host to half of another twinsome, while your second twin visits the other home. This is good during preschool days and later. Get them used to independent experiences which are separate from their interpair life early, in order to prepare them for a life of their own later on. Going alone on trips with Daddy or friends helps, too. When emergencies separate them, these brief previews will have cushioned the shock.

Picnics, family get-togethers, and a Christmas party take the place of some MOT meetings. Here the children have a chance to see other families of multiples so that both twins and nontwins, as well as Daddy, feel more "normal."

Without a dissenting voice all MOTs say, let housework go! Don't even *try* to be efficient—enjoy the babies and forget the dust. Put up plastic curtains, hide all ornaments, use paper plates and cups. There is plenty of time ahead for frills. Family frolics now build a serene feeling underneath all confusion.

Love and fun and plenty of discipline seem to be the secret of these big happy broods. Although all five children were indoors when I visited Shirley, there wasn't any crying and no egos whining for attention. I asked how she did it.

"I have to put my strength where it does the most good. If that happens to be the seat of their pants, okay! We've already worn out three flyswatters." She laughed as she pointed to a tattered one under the couch. "A flick doesn't hurt much, but it teaches them fast, like newspapers on a puppy. We've got five [now six] rambunctious, happy kids who love us and each other, because they've learned that rules are part of society. One of the first things John said when he came home from school was, 'Mommy, we have lots of good rules at school, too!' Children *like* discipline if you start early. It makes them secure."

Her big houseful of kids proved her methods work. So long as they don't hurt anyone else, they can work off tantrums unchecked in their room or the yard.

"Rage has to go somewhere," she said. "Get rid of it fast without mayhem or reruns later. Don't drive it deep to simmer."

Multiples may seem slower than singletons, but this is often only a misconception, for they communicate without words. Actually their social growth is much more rapid. They are used to sharing and to sensing the feelings of others.

One of a pair of boys in the club lorded it all over his twin, who couldn't read yet.

"You don't know nuthin'! Can't read! Can't write! Just a dumb-bell!"

For several days Chris endured the sneers, then neatly flattened his twin's bumptious ego. Lugging one of the volumes of the encyclopedia across the room, he dumped it in his tormentor's lap.

"Okay, big shot! Read to me!"

This same young genius listened patiently to a lecture on being a likable person, but frowned when his mother concluded, "Never forget, Chris, we're here in this world to help others!"

A few minutes later he was back tugging at her skirt.

"Hey, Mom—what are the others here for?"

Natural Childbirth

At another meeting the MOTs had a hot discussion on natural childbirth. One of them had experienced it most happily herself.

Another member brought a book, *Husband-Coached Childbirth*, by Dr. Robert A. Bradley, and some articles on the Lamaze method. "Childbirth is an athletic event," says Dr. Bradley, a Denver obstetrician, "and a husband is the best possible coach during pregnancy, labor, and birth itself."[5]

He teaches his mothers-to-be to strengthen their muscles weeks ahead of time through exercise, and thus eliminate pain during the first stage of childbirth. His *eight thousand cases* of husbands in the delivery room to encourage and sustain their wives are proof of his method. His patients *walk* back to bed and usually leave the hospital in a few hours.

Dr. Bradley also found simultaneous sleep patterns on the EEG, showing babies with dream patterns identical to those of their mothers. This is especially true of breast-fed babies, he said.

Women in labor without their husbands often transfer their affection to the doctor out of anxiety. But expectant fathers made superb labor-coaches. Their wives had less pain and later regarded it as a rich and pleasurable experience. Mutual love intensified, and husbands became better fathers. Their babies were placid, cried very little, accepted any food formula, and developed happy relationships.

Dr. Carl Goetsch, of the University of California Medical School in San Francisco, also urged the father's presence in the delivery room to help in natural childbirth without anesthetics.

"Except in unusual circumstances," he said, "the husband is a legitimate and useful member of the delivery-room team. He should never be considered an intruder." Dr. Goetsch had discovered this for himself when permitted to attend the birth of his first child. "I suddenly realized that I was functioning as a father should—that this was really the place I should be, not as a waiting-room clown." Later he played a key role in amending California law so that husbands could be admitted to the delivery room.

Yet elsewhere the picture is not so happy. So much publicity is given today to "medical heroics" and so little to preventive measures. Enormous government grants are awarded for research into such methods as induced labor. It is stated as a great advance that by 1972 pregnant women entering certain hospitals will have their babies during normal nine-to-five working hours! Dosing the woman with oxytocin about two weeks before term makes her expel the fetus "normally" in a few hours and at the doctors' convenience.

Since we know that multiple births do involve greater risks to both mothers and infants, obviously MOTs should be aware and alert to all these factors ahead of time. Ideally, before choosing an obstetrician, they should be acquainted with his attitudes and customary decisions here, for so much can be at stake.

By contrast to the oxytocin method of hastening labor, physicians at the University of California's San Diego School of Medicine give great thought to the question "Is the infant in the womb ready to face life?" They believe a difference in timing could well mean the difference between a normal healthy child and one headed down the road to disease or early death.

"We think we can tell exactly when a baby is ready to be born," Dr. Louis Gluck, professor of pediatrics there, stated. He estimated that 10, perhaps even 20, percent of infant mortality is caused by the newborn infant being brought out too soon, either by induction of labor or by cesarean section, with subsequent fatal respiratory problems.[6]

"If this is true of singletons, think how much worse it would be with twins!" exclaimed Marcia, whose twins were due the next month. "But—doesn't it hurt a lot?"

"That depends on us," Sally said, looking up from her notes. "Some women are in control clear through and think it's a wonderful experience. Others need a lot of reassurance but do quite well if they get it, and some are total flops. They skip classes, hate the whole deal, and—now get this!—they won't even consider breastfeeding!

"But what comes through to me," she went on, "is that these mothers don't just choose to *endure* the pain! They've learned how to breathe and to help ahead of time. Animals know how to go through labor—why shouldn't we learn? 'After it is over and you get back to your room,' one of the mothers I read about said, 'you just feel like you are flying.' And best of all, these babies aren't doped, and they get plenty of oxygen. University of California doctors find that even the nerve-block type of anesthetic passes into the fetus. Maybe it won't be enough to hurt a healthy baby, but it might if there are other stresses at the same time.

"If the mother is scared and breathes too fast and too shallowly, even a little anesthetic can produce brain damage in the last twin.[7] I'm converted, and I'm going to ask my doctor to let Bill stand by in the delivery room. I want my twins to choose their own time to be born—like good ripe fruit ready to fall from the tree!"

National Groups

No one is quite sure when and where the very first local twin club was organized, but a study group of the mothers of twenty-eight pairs of twins assembled in 1934 in Jamestown, New York. They were under the direction of Dr. Margaret Wylie, of the extension staff of Cornell University. How many similar groups sprang from this gathering is not known.

But in June, 1960, the first convention of the National Mothers of Twins Clubs was held in Canton, Ohio, with fifty-eight mothers there, representing thirty-three clubs from only nine states. Following this meeting National grew rapidly, incorporated, and chose their motto —"Where God Chooses the Members." In July, 1970, there were 245 member clubs in forty-four states with more than 8,500 members. Their annual conventions meet in various cities.

Although there are a number of informal local groups, most now affiliate with the national organization. Obviously these clubs meet a great need. Some of them put out valuable booklets at small cost. Others have their own newsletters—*The Twinsey Report, Carbon Copies, Double Exposure,* and the like.

One group even has a "Welcome Twin Wagon" in the hospital. Bearing books, pamphlets, dozens of diapers, and two kimonos, this is wheeled into the room of every new mother of multiples along with cheery and helpful advice. The clubs themselves often vie for catchy names, such as the Two Bits, Pair-a-Troopers, Mix 'n' Match, Twins or Better, Twice as Nice, and the Dual Jewels.

The members of National receive MOTC's bimonthly *Notebook,* a large bulletin filled with interesting news about twins everywhere. Research projects, in some of which members cooperate with doctors, on German measles, diabetes, hypnotic susceptibility, voice patterns, and the like are discussed. They have an international correspondent who brings together MOTs from England, Israel, and Australia who want pen pals.

A joke in the MOTC *Notebook* suggests that some mothers may at times tell "the facts of life" too early. A little boy who had been bubbling over at school at the prospect of a new baby suddenly became silent. Finally the teacher asked, "Whatever happened to that new baby?"

His eyes grew big and sad. "I think Mommy ate him!" he told her mournfully.

One club has a subgroup called MOPS, for Mothers of Pre-Schoolers. Many have private charities of hospitals and needy twins.

The permanent address of the National MOTC is 612 Wallace Drive, Wayne, Pennsylvania 19087. Their policy is noncommercial, nonpartisan, nonprofit, nonracial, and nonsectarian. Among their stated purposes are participation in research, cooperation with all groups having related interests, and increasing the awareness of the individuality of each twin.

Chapters can usually be located through your local chamber of commerce, the library, or the women's editor of your newspaper. They also publish a valuable list of helpful and inexpensive booklets put out by local groups and child study groups, for twin toddlers up to college.

In the northeastern states there is a Mothers of Triplets Association with over two hundred members. They, too, have an annual convention each spring in New York City.

An Organization for Twins Themselves

There is still another twin club—this one not for mothers but for the twins themselves—the International Twins Association, Inc. It began about forty years ago with a picnic at Silver Lake, Indiana, and mushroomed into a national, then an international group. Today twins come from all points of the compass to the annual Labor Day Convention.

Membership varies in ITA; there are probably six hundred sets of active twins, with some fifteen hundred on the mailing list. Many local clubs—some with newsletters and as many as five hundred on their own mailing lists—are eligible but not always on the International lists. The latter publishes two or three newsletters yearly for members and the libraries of other organizations.

There are no age limits, and contests are held annually for the youngest, oldest, most identical, and least alike, and for a king and queen. Although mainly a social group, they, too, take part in research projects such as fingerprint and hereditary studies, blood grouping, and ESP studies.

"You name the research project, and I'll bet there is a set of twins in it somewhere!" says one pair, the Rowe sisters, who are twin models and photographers and sign their letters and records "Twincerely Yours."

International's letterhead states: "Organized by and for twins, a non-profit organization to promote the spiritual, intellectual, and social welfare of twins throughout the world." Officers are chosen at the annual conventions. The organization has no formal permanent headquarters, but one enthusiastic pair of members, who first attended as small children in 1934, has volunteered to have their names and address listed as such. Twins who would like to join may write Mrs. Judy Stillwagon and Mrs. Julie Kirk at 114 North Lafayette Drive, Muncie, Indiana 47303.

You can also write to another pair mentioned in Chapter 10—LaVona and LaVelda Rowe—who put out a newsletter going to as many as three thousand twins. Their permanent mailing address is 608 South Madison Street, Iowa City, Iowa 52240. There have been twins in their family for six hundred years.

The girls say, "We have seventeen sets of living twin cousins on both sides of the family," so they must know quite a bit about twins!

Among twins and mothers of twins across America one point is constantly argued and never settled: Should the twins be dressed alike?

Think it over. It's very expensive in time and energy as well as money. Usually one twin gets dirty faster; or a twin tears a garment or loses a sock, and matching ones must be discarded. You can't accept hand-me-downs or exchanges. And some mothers think identical dress keeps twins from becoming real individuals. Some twins, however, adore it, and even as adults they keep it up. (It's an attention-getter, and it may help the shy ones.)

For twins who follow the golden rule, as Judge Crail summed it up, there are two laughs from one joke, two thrills for the same joy. "It is happiness just to live when one is born a twin."

BIBLIOGRAPHICAL NOTES

CHAPTER 1

[1] Charles S. Crail, *My Twin Joe* (Garden City, N.Y.: Country Life Press), 1932.

[2] R. E. L. Masters and Jean Houston, *The Varieties of Psychedelic Experience* (New York: Holt, Rinehart and Winston), 1966. By permission of the authors.

[3] Horatio H. Newman, *Multiple Human Births: Twins, Triplets, Quadruplets and Quintuplets,* American Association for Advancement of Science (New York: Doubleday, Doran & Co., Inc.), 1940; Horatio H. Newman, *Twins and Supertwins: A Study of Twins, Triplets, Quadruplets and Quintuplets,* Advancement of Science Series #1 (London: Hutchinson), 1942; Horatio H. Newman, Frank N. Freeman, and Karl J. Holzinger, *Twins: A Study of Heredity and Environment* (Chicago: University of Chicago Press), 1966.

[4] Edward D. Radin, *12 Against Crime* (New York: G. P. Putnam's Sons), 1950.

CHAPTER 2

[1] George M. Gould and Walter L. Pyle, *Anomalies and Curiosities of Medicine* (New York: Sydenham Publishers), 1937.

[2] *Today's Health,* March, 1967.

[3] *Science News Letter,* December 19, 1953.

[4] M. G. Bulmer, *The Biology of Twinning in Man* (New York: Oxford University Press), 1970.

[5] L. Gedda and G. Brenci, "Human Monozygotic and Plurizygotic Multiple Births: Heredity and Hormone Action," *Acta Geneticae Medicae et Gemellologiae,* 14:109–131 (1965).

[6] *Today's Health,* March, 1967.

[7] Betsy Gehman, *Twins: Twice the Trouble, Twice the Fun* (Philadelphia and New York: J. B. Lippincott Company), 1965.

8 *Ibid.*

9 Gedda and Brenci, *loc. cit. Guinness Book of World Records* (New York: Bantam Books), 1970 edition.

10 Robert Ripley, *Believe It or Not Omnibus* (New York: Simon and Schuster), 1929.

11 Gedda and Brenci, *loc. cit.*, p. 110.

CHAPTER 3

1 Jean Rostand and André Tétry, *An Atlas of Human Genetics* (London: Hutchinson and Co., Ltd.), 1964.

2 Gene Lowall, "Killer-on-the-Loose: The Sinister Shadow of 'XYY,'" *Argosy*, February, 1968.

3 Jane E. Brody, "Will Our Baby Be Normal?" *Woman's Day*, August, 1969.

4 David M. Rorvik, "The Brave New World of the Unborn," *Look*, November 4, 1969.

5 Kurt Benirschke, "Spontaneous Chimerism in Mammals," *Current Topics in Pathology* (Hanover, N.H.: Dartmouth Medical School), Vol. 51.

6 Malou, Benirschke, and Hoefnagel, "XX/XY Chimerism in a Tricolored Male Cat," *Cytogenetics*, 6:228–241 (1967).

7 Rostand and Tétry, *op. cit.*

8 John Lentz, "How Medical Progress Has Hastened the Passing of the Side Show," *Today's Health*, March, 1964.

9 *Good Housekeeping*, May, 1967.

10 Rorvik, *loc. cit.*

11 Gordon R. Taylor, *The Biological Time Bomb* (New York and Cleveland: World Publishing Co.), 1967. AP dispatch, April 2, 1970.

12 *Ibid.*

CHAPTER 4

1 Tacoma (Washington) *News Tribune*, January 12, 1959.

2 Herman E. Krimmel, "Blood Brothers," *Fate*, May–June, 1951.

3 Bard Lindeman, "The Twins Who Found Each Other," *Saturday Evening Post*, March 21, 1964.

4 Radin, *op. cit.* George Kent, "The Case of the Third Twin," *Reader's Digest*, November, 1951.

5 James Shields, *Monozygotic Twins Brought Up Apart and Brought Up Together: An Investigation into the Genetic and Environmental Causes of Variation in Personality* (London: Oxford University Press), 1962.

CHAPTER 5

1 Rorvik, *loc. cit.* Barbara Yunkers, "The Baby Bubble," *Ladies' Home Journal*, September, 1969. Ora Mendels, "A Revolution in Childbirth," *Ladies' Home Journal*, Winter, 1963. Copley News Service, January 22, 1967. Elizabeth Kennedy, "Baby Bubble Sequel," *Ladies' Home Journal*, October, 1971.

2 *Life*, March 31, 1967.

[3] Morton M. Hunt, "Dr. Kallmann's 7,000 Twins," *Saturday Evening Post,* November 6, 1954.

[4] Philadelphia and New York: J. B. Lippincott Company, 1967.

[5] New York: Basic Books, Inc., 1963.

[6] AP dispatch, November 1, 1968.

[7] Tom Buckley, "The Transsexual Operation," *Esquire,* April, 1967. AP dispatch, December 28, 1970.

[8] *Crime as Destiny* (Germany, 1929; London, 1931).

[9] Dora Jane Hamblin, "They Are 'Idiot Savants'—Wizards of the Calendar," *Life,* March 18, 1966. Bob Gaines, "The Memory Twins Who Baffle Science," *Family Weekly,* March 6, 1966. *The New York Times,* November 5, 1965.

CHAPTER 6

[1] Joseph F. Goodavage, *Astrology, The Space Age Science* (West Nyack, N.Y.: Parker Publishing Co., Inc.), 1966.

[2] Harvey Day, "Linked Lives," *Prediction,* Vol. 31, No. 8 (1965).

[3] *Strange Medical Facts,* Fall, 1953.

[4] *Tomorrow,* Spring, 1961. *Fate,* August, 1956.

[5] AP dispatch, September 28, 1959.

[6] Goodavage, *op. cit.*

[7] *Fate,* May, 1962.

[8] Goodavage, *op. cit.*

[9] *Fate,* June, 1959. *Coronet* (undated clipping).

[10] *Archives of General Psychiatry,* October, 1964. Tom Allen, "The Twins Who Willed Their Death," *Fate,* November, 1964.

[11] From the foreword to Arthur W. Osborn, *The Meaning of Personal Existence* (Wheaton, Ill.: Quest Books), 1968.

[12] Ralph Shirley, *The Problem of Rebirth* (London: Rider and Co.), n.d.

CHAPTER 7

[1] *Good Housekeeping,* April, 1965.

[2] Amram Scheinfeld, *Twins and Supertwins* (Philadelphia and New York: J. B. Lippincott Company), 1967.

[3] A. E. Farrell, "The Happy Miracle in Lima, Ohio," *Good Housekeeping,* September, 1963. Myron Cope, "How to Be a Loser with Four Aces," *Saturday Evening Post,* June 6, 1964.

[4] H. H. Martin, "The Mystery Quints of Argentina," *Saturday Evening Post,* January 25, 1964. *Life,* December 13, 1963. *Time,* July 25, 1955, and July 28, 1958.

[5] *Time,* September 20, 1963. H. H. Martin, "The Other Babies Who Broke the Odds," *Saturday Evening Post,* January 18, 1964, and H. H. Martin, *Saturday Evening Post,* October 3, 1964.

[6] *Ladies' Home Journal,* December, 1963.

[7] Dorothy C. Disney, "My Life, My Children," *Ladies' Home Journal,* December, 1963. Phyllis Wright, "The Fischer Quints at Two," *Ladies' Home Journal,* January, 1966. Also see *Saturday Evening Post,* July 31 and December 18, 1965.

8 "Africa's Only Living Quintuplets," *Ebony,* December, 1966.

9 *Redbook,* March, 1966.

10 "Artificial Inovulation—A Startling New Way to Have a Baby," *Mc-Call's,* May, 1969. "The Control of Life" Series, *Life,* September 10, 1965.

CHAPTER 8

1 Gehman, *op. cit.*

2 *International Journal of Parapsychology,* Autumn, 1961.

3 Hamilton (Ontario) *Spectator,* April 7, 1966. Letter to the authors.

4 London: Cassell and Co., Ltd., 1960.

5 "Telepathic Impressions: A Review of 35 New Cases," *Proceedings,* American Society for Psychical Research, Vol. 29 (June, 1970).

6 *Fate,* September, 1960.

7 *Tomorrow,* Winter, 1962.

8 Vincent H. Gaddis, "With Brain Destroyed They Live and Think," *Fate,* Summer, 1948. Benito F. Reyes, *Scientific Evidence of the Existence of the Soul* (Wheaton, Ill.: Quest Books), 1970.

9 New York: W. W. Norton and Co., 1963.

10 *Science,* October 15, 1965. *Newsletter,* International Parapsychology Foundation, Inc., January–February, 1966.

11 Montague Ullman, Stanley Krippner, and Sol Feldstein, "Experimentally Induced Telepathic Effects in Dreams," Report of Maimonides Hospital, Brooklyn, N.Y., March, 1966. Maimonides Medical Center Reports, "Dream Studies and Telepathy," January, 1969, and "Extrasensory Electroencephalographic Induction Progress Report," February, 1969. Alan Vaughn, "A Dream Grows in Brooklyn," *Psychic,* February, 1970.

12 Edmund Gurney, F. W. H. Myers, and Frank Podmore (London: Trubner, 1886; New York: E. P. Dutton and Co., 1918).

13 *Proceedings,* Society for Psychical Research, Vol. XLV.

14 Newman, *op. cit.*

15 Dorothy Bomar and Robert A. Bradley, *Psychic Phenomena: Revelations and Experiences* (West Nyack, N.Y.: Parker Publishing Co., Inc.), 1967.

16 *A Search for the Truth* (New York: William Morrow and Co.), 1967.

CHAPTER 9

1 C. J. S. Thompson, *The Mystery and Lore of Monsters* (New Hyde Park, N.Y.: University Books), 1968. Gould and Pyle, *op. cit.*

2 *Today's Health,* March, 1964.

3 "Rare Change from 'Us' to 'Me,' " *Life,* June 25, 1965.

4 Al Hirshberg, "So Tiny, So Much to Love," *Good Housekeeping,* April, 1962. *Time,* April 11, 1955.

5 *Life,* April 8, 1966.

6 *True,* January, 1964.

CHAPTER 10

1 *International Journal of Parapsychology,* Autumn, 1961.

2 *Ebony,* September, 1965.

3 "A Brother Is to Love," *Look,* February 13, 1962.

4 Shota Ushio, "Second Japanese Twin Is Considered Senior," UPI dispatch, November 10, 1968.

5 Chicago: University of Chicago Press, 1966.

6 UPI dispatch, June, 1969.

7 *Ebony,* November, 1968.

8 "Dear Abby vs Dear Ann," *McCall's,* November, 1957.

9 Peter Packer, *Death of the Other Self* (New York: Cowles Book Company, Inc.), 1970.

CHAPTER 11

1 Fred Gettings, *The Book of the Hand—An Illustrated History of Palmistry* (London: Paul Hamlyn, Ltd.), 1965. Noel Jaquin, *The Human Hand, The Living Symbol* (New York: Robert McBride, Inc.), 1959. Walter Sorrell, *The Story of the Human Hand* (New York: Bobbs-Merrill Co.), 1967. Dr. Charlotte Wolff, *The Human Hand* (New York: Alfred A. Knopf), 1943.

2 Dr. David Rosenthal, *The Genain Quadruplets* (New York: Basic Books, Inc.), 1963.

3 *Diagrams of the Unconscious—Handwriting and Personality in Measurement, Experience and Analysis* (New York: Grune and Stratton), 1948.

4 Stockholm: Almquist and Wiksell, n.d.

5 Ellic Howe, *Astrology: A Recent History Including the Untold Story of Its Role in World War II* (New York: Walker and Co.), 1968.

6 John M. Addey, "Astrological Twins," *The Astrological Journal,* Winter, 1966–1967. Day, *loc. cit.*

7 *Fate,* January, 1964.

8 Addey, *loc. cit.*

9 Day, *loc. cit.*

10 Goodavage, *op. cit.*

11 London: The English Universities Press, Ltd., 1964.

12 Letter to the authors.

13 "Astrology and Statistical Investigation," *In Search,* Vol. 1, No. 3 (Autumn, 1958).

14 Chicago: Henry Regnery Company, 1967.

15 Vol. 98 (1967), p. 1002.

16 Vincent H. Gaddis, *Mysterious Fires and Lights* (New York: David McKay Company, Inc.), 1967.

17 Paul Grof, letters to the authors.

ASTROLOGICAL DATA:

The Brodie Siamese Twins: Septemper 16, 1951, 41° 31′ N., 90° 26′ W. Roger, 8:55 A.M. CST. Roger had 29:48 of Libra rising. The 29th degree is called the "Fatalistic Degree" by many astrologers, and here it is his Ascendant, signifying the body. Rodney, who survived surgery for some years, was born at 9 A.M. with 0:54 Scorpio rising. (Data from Miss Mary Peter, who knew one of the nurses.) Separation surgery performed December 17, 1952.

Michel Gauquelin, November 13, 1928, in Paris, hour unknown. Sun about 21 Scorpio. (Data from *The Astrological Journal.*)

Eugen Jonas, November 6, 1928, in Nitra, Czechoslovakia, with 4:22 Scorpio rising and the sun in 13½ Scorpio; moon in early Virgo conjunct Neptune. (Data from *The Astrological Journal.*)

CHAPTER 12

1 Margaret Mead, *Sex and Temperament in Three Primitive Societies* (New York: New American Library), 1950.
2 September, 1965.
3 Alfred Metraux, *Voodoo* (New York: Oxford University Press), 1959.
4 Ann Landers, "Say No to Your Kids—They'll Love You for It," *Family Circle,* June, 1968. Abigail Van Buren, "Are You a Mini-Mother?" *Family Circle,* March, 1969. *Ladies' Home Journal,* June, 1968. Letters to the authors.
5 Mee Morningside, "Strange But True," *True,* June, 1953.

CHAPTER 13

1 *Archives of Neurology and Psychiatry,* August, 1958. AP dispatch, July 25, 1968. *Fate,* April, 1966.

CHAPTER 14

1 *Psychology Today,* June, 1968.
2 La Leche League, *The Womanly Art of Breast Feeding* (Franklin Park, Ill.). Mike and Marilyn Ferguson, *Champagne Living on a Beer Budget* (New York: G. P. Putnam's Sons), 1968.
3 Frank G. Slaughter, *Your Body and Your Mind* (New York: New American Library), 1953.
4 Phyllis Wright, undated clipping from "Medicine Today," *Ladies' Home Journal.*
5 *Husband-Coached Childbirth* (New York: Harper & Row), 1965. Also see Dr. Bradley's articles in *Psychosomatics,* November–December, 1962; *Medical Opinion and Review,* December, 1966; and *St. Anthony Messenger,* December, 1968.
6 San Diego *Union,* May 28, 1967; June 26, 1970; and November 6, 1970.
7 "Anesthetic Held Danger to Baby During Delivery," Los Angeles *Times,* March 11, 1970.

SELECTED BIBLIOGRAPHY

Asimov, Isaac. *The Human Body.* New York: New American Library, 1963.

Auerbach, Charlotte. *The Science of Genetics.* New York: Harper's Modern Science Series, 1961.

Benirschke, Kurt. "Spontaneous Chimerism in Mammals: A Critical Review," *Current Topics in Pathology,* Vol. 51. Hanover, N.H.: Dartmouth Medical School.

Bradley, Robert A. *Husband-Coached Childbirth.* New York: Harper & Row, 1965.

Bulmer, M. G. *The Biology of Twinning in Man.* New York and London: Oxford University Press, 1970.

Child Study Association (New York). "And Then There Were Two."

Clendening, Logan. *Behind the Doctor.* New York: Alfred A. Knopf, Inc., 1933.

Frazer, Sir James G. *The Golden Bough: A Study in Magic and Religion.* New York: The Macmillan Company, 1940.

Garrigan, Owen. *Man's Intervention in Nature.* New York: Hawthorn Books, Inc., 1967.

Gedda, Luigi. *Acta Geneticae Medicae et Gemellologiae,* Vol. XIV, No. 2.

———. *Acta Geneticae Medicae et Gemellologiae,* October, 1960.

———. *I Gemelli della Val d'Aosta.* Rome, Italy.

———. *Twins in History and Science.* Springfield, Ill.: Charles C. Thomas, 1961.

Gould, George M., and Pyle, Walter L. *Anomalies and Curiosities of Medicine.* New York: Sydenham Publishers, 1937.

201

Graham, Phyllis. *The Care and Feeding of Twins*. New York: Harper & Row, 1955.

Haggard, Howard W. *Devils, Drugs and Doctors*. New York: Pocket Books, 1946.

Koch, Helen L. *Twins and Twin Relations*. Chicago: Chicago University Press, 1966.

Larousse Encyclopedia of Mythology. New York: Prometheus Press, 1959.

Malouf, Najla, Benirschke, K., and Hoefnagel, D. "XX/XY Chimerism in a Tricolored Male Cat," *Cytogenetics*, 6:228–241 (1967).

Mothers of Twins Clubs booklets. "For Two, Please," Berwyn, Pa. "No Two Alike," Cleveland, Ohio. "Twins, A Guide to Their Education," Main Line. "Twins in Infancy," Westchester, N.Y.

Newman, Horatio H. *Multiple Human Births: Twins, Triplets, Quadruplets and Quintuplets*. American Association for Advancement of Science. New York: Doubleday, Doran & Co., Inc., 1940.

———. *Twins and Supertwins: A Study of Twins, Triplets, Quadruplets and Quintuplets*. Advancement of Science Series #1. London: Hutchinson, 1942.

———, Freeman, Frank N., and Holzinger, Karl J. *Twins: A Study of Heredity and Environment*. Chicago: University of Chicago Press, 1966.

Rhine, J. B., ed., with Brier, Robert. *Parapsychology Today*. New York: The Citadel Press, 1968.

———. *The Reach of the Mind*. New York: Apollo, 1961.

Rhine, Louisa E. *ESP in Life and Lab*. New York: The Macmillan Company, 1967.

———. *Hidden Channels of the Mind*. New York: William Morrow and Company, 1961.

Rostand, Jean, and Tétry, André. *An Atlas of Human Genetics*. London: Hutchinson and Co., Ltd., 1964.

Scheinfeld, Amram. *Twins and Supertwins*. Philadelphia and New York: J. B. Lippincott Company, 1967.

———. *Women and Men*. London: Chatto and Windus, 1947.

Shields, James, *Monozygotic Twins Brought Up Apart and Brought Up Together: An Investigation into the Genetic and Environmental Causes of Variation in Personality*. London: Oxford University Press, 1962.

Slaughter, Frank G. *Your Body and Your Mind*. New York: New American Library, 1954. (Original title: *Medicine for Moderns*. New York: Julian Messner, Inc., 1953.)

Wilde, Gerrit Jan S. "Inheritance of Personality Traits," *Acta Psychologica*, 22 (1964), 37–51.

INDEX

"Abby, Dear," 170–171
Addresses
  birth-defects center, 29
  clubs, 192, 193
Adoption, prenatal, 39
Africa, twins, 15, 165
  See also South Africa
Ages, record, 14
Allergies, 186
Alpha waves, 107–109
Amniocentesis, 28
Anesthetics, 79, 189–191
Animals, 24, 32, 96–97
Anomalies
  animal, 24, 114–115
  human, 22, 29, 38, 114–128
    chromosomal, 26–29, 126–127
Anthony, Mark, 168
Apparitions, 112–113
Argentina, quintuplets, 83–86
Armadillos, 24, 39
Artificial insemination, 20, 39, 97
Astrological Journal, The (periodical), 152–153
Astrology, 131, 149–161
Atkinson, Florence, 124–125
Atkinson, Napit and Prissana, 124–125
Attitudes, mother's sexual, 186–187
Auerbach, Dr. Charlotte, 41, 62
Axe quadruplets, 81–82, 88

"Baby bubble," 56
Behrendt, Dr. Thomas, 107–108
Benirschke, Dr. Kurt, 24–25, 31, 39
Biddenden Maids, 115
Biological clocks, 159
Birth, order of, 32, 49, 54, 144
Birth-defects center, 29
Birth-robe, *see* Chorion
"Birth suit," 56
Births, days apart, 35–38
Blazek, Rosa and Josepha, 121
Blood
  Rh factor, 48
  transfusions, 20, 29–30
  types, 30–31, 48
Boy-girl fraternals, 136, 138, 163
Boy-girl "identicals," 14, 17, 32
Bradley, Dr. Robert A., 111, 189
Brain, destroyed, 106–107
Breast-feeding, 56, 85, 87, 121, 163, 186–187, 189–190
Breathing, 19, 55–56, 79, 191
Brian, Joan, 102–103
Brodie Siamese twins, 123, 158, 199
Bulmer, Dr. M. G., 19
Buzby, Dr. Dallas E., 112

"Calendar encyclopedias," 63–64
Calves, 24, 30, 96–97
  See also Freemartins